PSYCHIC SUMMER

"It becomes a ghostly Chappaquiddick with two young women mysteriously drowned 100 years before, unfolding a tale of malevolence and guilt."

—*St. Louis Post-Dispatch*

"This is a true story, documented by notes taken during each visit of the sisters. And it's a gripping one. It can only be told now because the house where it all happened burned to the ground."

—*Newport News Daily Press*

"An amazing psychic chiller . . . objects flying through the air, psychic photos, spirits spewing obscenities . . ."

—*Publishers Weekly*

PSYCHIC SUMMER

ARNOLD COPPER
AND
CORALEE LEON

A DELL BOOK

Published by
DELL PUBLISHING CO., INC.
1 Dag Hammarskjold Plaza
New York, N.Y. 10017

ISBN: 0-440-17166-0

Reprinted by arrangement with
The Dial Press
Printed in the United States of America
First Dell printing—July 1977
Second Dell printing—August 1977
Third Dell printing—September 1977
Fourth Dell printing—October 1977

On a cold Sunday afternoon in January 1975, I was invited to tea, along with about twenty other guests (all professional people, none of whom I had met before) at the home of my good friend Landine Manigault. During the party someone began guessing astrological signs, and there followed a series of personal accounts of psychic experiences, dealings in ESP, and other mysteries—for there is hardly a person alive who has not had some brush with the supernatural, or at least the unexplainable. Of course there were skeptics among us: "You don't really believe that stuff," someone said. And then a young man seated on the floor beside my chair said, "Well, I *never* believed any of it until one summer a few years ago when it happened to me." He proceeded to tell the most chilling story of a strange summer he had spent at a beach house with three friends and a homemade Ouija. As he finished the story, one woman was so overcome that she had to be taken out of the room in fright, crying.

I turned to this young man, a stranger, whose name was Arnold Copper. "Have you ever thought of publishing that?" I asked. He had not—but was persuaded that it was indeed a story that would interest many people. And that was the beginning of our collaboration—and of *Psychic Summer*.

We therefore wish to express our thanks and our affection

to our friend
Landine Legendre Manigault
who brought us together.

C.L.

The events described in this book are true. Some of the characters are well-known personalities whom many readers will recognize. Most of the names have been changed to protect those who shared with me a bizarre ordeal that took place in a house on Fire Island in the summer of 1967. For a long time I was unable to publish the story; it seemed dangerous to the people who lived in the neighborhood to reveal the strange happenings that took place there. But as of autumn 1974, the house no longer existed, the people had moved away, and I was free to tell my story.

A.C.

PSYCHIC SUMMER

PROLOGUE

Summer 1966

We lay practically naked in the blazing midsummer sun, baking our bodies until we could hardly breathe. At last we could stand it no longer; we had to get into the water. We ran down the beach, our soles searing at every step, and plunged headlong into the breakers.

There were about six of us together on the beach at Fire Island that day. When I came up from my dive I continued swimming alone, away from the others, away from the shore. I felt the exhilaration of my muscles pulling and stretching after all that time lying in the sun. I enjoyed the rhythm of breathing and stroking. It felt good to swim. Finally I stopped to rest, and looked back. I was astonished at the distance I had covered. I must have been several hundred yards from shore and considerably west of the beach in front of our house. Then I realized that I was still moving away from shore. The current must have sped my swim, and was now pulling me steadily outward and southward. I saw my friends struggling to shore, but nobody turned back to see where I was. Had they forgotten I was with them? Or did they think I had swum back to the beach already?

I felt an alarm in the pit of my belly. I forced my legs out behind me and began swimming toward shore. I swam thirty or forty strokes, then stopped. I had made no headway at all against the current, and now I was drifting farther out. My arms ached and trembled. I forced myself again, stroking and kicking with all my strength against the tide. But my tired body was no match for its force.

And then I felt the first downward pull, and was filled with terror. It was as if my body had become suddenly leaden in the normally buoyant water, as if my own weight were dragging me down.

The sun was scorching my face and the top of my head, and turning the surface of the sea into a white-hot glare that shot into my eyes like needles. I began to feel chilled. The water mingled with the suntan lotion and rolled into my already stinging eyes. I was practically blind, and weak and helpless, and frustrated to the point of madness. I squinted toward the beach. The houses were unfamiliar, and the few figures on the beach looked frighteningly small. I felt totally alone, totally helpless in that vast ocean. The thought terrified me.

The downward pull was unmistakable now. I resisted, trying to kick my legs up to make myself horizontal at the surface. Still I felt myself being dragged under. I tried to turn on my back. Relax, I told myself. Concentrate on relaxing. But I was being pulled down—out and down—in spite of my strength, in spite of my will. I squeezed my eyes shut as I felt my face going under. I struggled with all my strength. I had no thoughts at all, just the instincts of my body struggling to save itself. I broke the surface, gasped for air, and was immediately pulled down under again. I forced myself upward and managed to shout once, weakly, for help. My cry sounded pitifully feeble to me in the rushing of the water. I had no hope. The ocean was sucking and pulling me relentlessly down. My mind lost its continuity. I felt bright explosions in my head and in my eyes. My thoughts whirled and canceled one another out. There was no sequence to anything, but neither was there fear anymore. I felt the water's pull and felt somehow soothed, comforted. Then my lungs began to burn, and part of me struggled again, not only against the water but against the final surrender. But I could struggle no longer. My strength was gone. I remember nothing more.

I felt utterly relaxed. There was something straight and rigid against my back, but soft next to my skin. I was lying down. My face and the skin of my legs felt warm. There were tiny tingles and itches all over my body. But they didn't seem to have anything to do with me, and it did not occur to me to do anything about them. Involuntarily, my eyes opened. There was a blur of dazzling whiteness—they shut reflexively and I felt moisture around my lids. I felt my fingers move lightly over the surface beneath me, feeling a strange familiarity. A sense of awareness crept gradually through my whole body, as if the various dissociated molecules were beginning to hold together again. I cracked my eyes open, deliberately and cautiously. Gradually out of the glare there emerged several figures. I began to be aware of sounds. Murmurs and hushed tones of human voices. And a steady strong rhythm in the background. The ocean! Something inside me snapped, and I realized fully who I was. It was like waking up from sleep—or something like sleep.

There were several people around me. I was lying on a towel—that was the softness—on the wooden deck of someone's house. I tried to raise myself on my elbows, but they were utterly weak. And then I remembered the terrible struggle in the water. I sank back. A friend's voice reassured me that everything was going to be all right.

Later, my friends told me how I had been saved. A woman on the beach—who turned out to be actress Chita Rivera—miraculously heard my cry for help. She quickly dispatched her friend Tom with a raft. At the same time, one of my friends realized I was in trouble and dived into the water. They had no way of knowing, as they hoisted my body onto the raft, if they had reached me in time. And then there was the long way back, an incredible ordeal even with the buoyant raft. They dragged me up on the beach and began the ritual of resuscitation. Then they brought me up to the deck of this house, where I lay unconscious for an uneasy few minutes. I remembered nothing of my rescue. I only remembered the terrifying sensation of being pulled under the water, and a strange sense of well-being during the final moments of awareness.

Death would have been so easy, I thought to myself.

FIRST ENCOUNTER

Friday, June 30, 1967

I was very much alive the following summer, and feeling on top of the world as I packed suitcases, books, records, and other necessities into my brand-new beige Mercedes Benz. It was a great day in a great year. I had made a name for myself as an interior designer; the money was flowing in, and I counted among my friends diplomats, movie stars, designers, artists, writers, academicians. I was also beginning a small fashion business, designing men's and women's clothes, and this had been well received by the press. My apartment was a parlor floor-through in New York City's West Village, a district of quaint old town houses with courtyards and gardens and narrow winding streets. That afternoon I was leaving for the weekend beach house which I had rented for the rest of the summer with three friends.

I was in jeans that morning, and my sleeves were rolled up. The morning air was warm, but with a breeze a few shades cooler, a reminder that it was early summer. I slammed the trunk lid closed and went to fetch my twin cocker spaniel puppies—three-month-old blonds named Joshua and Rachel—who the previous week had eaten the softer centers out of my poker chips and shat red, white, and blue for two days. I put them squirming into the back seat, got in and started the engine, pulled away from the narrow sidewalk, and headed uptown to pick up two of my co-renters. Up in the West Sixties, Michael was sitting on his front steps with a suitcase. He was a sculptor, about twenty-five years old, with dark good looks and an intense earnestness about life that charmed everyone. He threw his things into the trunk and hopped into the car. Across town on the East Side, Howard and his doorman made two trips each with water skis, sailing gear, many albums, and clothing. Howard was one of the youngest motion picture distributors in the business. He went after everything with enthusiasm and determination, and always demanded the best of himself. He loved to socialize, and was always surrounded by women who often did not realize that pragmatic Howard had a vulnerable, romantic side, too.

It was just one o'clock and quite warm by the time we were through the Midtown Tunnel and into the thickening holiday traffic. We were in very good spirits and eager to leave the pace and politics of the city behind us.

It took an hour and a half to drive to Sayville, a small but buzzing town on Great South Bay, the bay between Long Island and Fire Island—buzzing because that was where everyone stopped to shop just before getting on the ferry that would take them to the community of Fire Island Pines, known simply as The Pines. We made a final stop at the supermarket to pick up groceries and then headed for the ferry docks.

Getting everything onto the ferryboat was a major performance. We backed the car up to the ramp and loaded our gear onto the platform. Then I had to put the car in the parking lot while the others began carrying things onto the boat. Other weekenders were busily doing the same thing, and there was general good-natured chaos on the wharf. Laundry bags and suitcases and other soft waterproof packages were thrown up onto the bow of the boat. Paper bags and small cases went inside the broad, low-ceilinged cabin where the passengers could sit on pewlike benches for the twenty-minute ride. The three of us climbed the metal steps up to the top deck.

We stood quietly at the rail with Rachel and Joshua, watching the bay water turn mossy green in the midafternoon sun. The water was surprisingly active, churned by passing speedboats and other ferries and the wind that blew steadily from the East. Clouds were gathering behind us, but the sky was huge and seemed to rest like a dome on the flat terrain of Long Island, now at our backs, and the narrow spit of land ahead.

Fire Island. A thirty-three-mile-long sandbar nowhere more than a quarter of a mile wide stretching almost due east-west parallel to the south shore of Long Island. I had heard Fire Island was named by whalers in the eighteenth century, who on impenetrably foggy nights built fires on the beach to warn boats away from the treacherous currents—or, said some, to lure boats onto the shoals for salvage. Ever since the birth of the New England shipping and fishing trades, hundreds of ships had been wrecked in the unpredictable tides—the bane of mariners and the lure of modern treasure hunters who explored the ships' carcasses in rubber suits and fishlike fins in search of bounty and adventure.

The lumbering old ferry rumbled into its berth at the dock of The Pines and disgorged its passengers. We joined the hubbub of people scurrying to get their belongings off the boat and into the hand wagons padlocked to the fence near the harbor. We found our wagon, loaded it up, and carted everything to the taxi stand, where we had to reload it into a sand taxi, one of a fleet of army-green jeeps that puttered along the beach. I took the wagon back to the fence (every house had its wagon for carting groceries and supplies up and down the boardwalk), and we all packed ourselves into the taxi.

The only reason you couldn't see from one side

of the narrow island to the other is that the center rose in a series of dunes filled with low misshapen pine trees and big modern architects' houses. Most of the houses were built of weathered gray clapboard; some were very imposing and large (they replaced the houses that had been swept away by Hurricane Donna in 1960) and all were built up on stilts, partly to get them above water level, partly for the ocean view. Most of the houses were ultramodern, cantilevered, and with great expanses of glass. They were not beautiful, but in their setting of gnarled, twisted, weathered trees and rolling dunes, they looked as though they belonged there, and had been there forever. Behind the big houses was the ocean boardwalk, linked to the bay road by a system of narrow raised walks that laced through the dunes. Between these secondary boardwalks were small, older cottages nestled in the dunes—one-story houses with green asbestos roofs, all on low pilings with open crawl spaces beneath. All had decks and, because some of the big houses that had been washed away had not yet been replaced, a few of the cottages had ocean views. Across the road, a high jump up, was the bay-side boardwalk, more houses, then the small narrow sand beach from which the fishing piers and boat docks protruded into the shallow bay. The system of boardwalks at The Pines was so thorough that you hardly had to set foot in the sand to get from one end of the community to the other.

Our sand taxi jolted us along the firm, damp

sand beside the water's edge; the ocean was calm with small waves that lapped serenely on the shore. Cherry Grove, the wild and infamous part of Fire Island known for its gay population and scandalous drag parties, was in the other direction a couple of miles down the beach. Our house was at the far end of The Pines, toward Water Island, the next community to the east. The Pines was a larger community whose main population was made up of professional people like ourselves: TV people, fashion editors, writers, the occasional Beautiful Person, visitors from Europe and South America, and whole families including nannies and kids. The population was spread out, however, and the beach was usually sparsely peopled at our end, which appealed strongly to my preference for privacy.

During the day, one could go over to the bay to clam and crab and fish, or to water-ski or sail. The ocean side was for swimming and sunbathing. At night, one could go to two discotheques a fifteen-minute walk down the boardwalk. One was the Sandpiper, a disco that was always packed, very smoky and dark. We usually went to the Boatel, a harbor club where mainlanders moored their cabin cruisers and yawls and came to gape at the throng of heaving bodies dancing to the best sound on the Island. The Boatel was a cross between indoors and outdoors. Its walls were really Bahama shutters that were propped up at night to form roof overhangs over the edges of a huge deck. Dancing went on inside, where it was dark and moody, with smoky red lighting. The bright lights were outside on the deck, where one went to sit and have a drink and talk. All the most fashionable and best-dressed people went there, done up for the purpose of being seen. One would see the latest, hottest movie star or the socialite of the hour at the Boatel.

We finally arrived at our ocean house. The fourth member of our renting cooperative was already there: François, a recently divorced French fashion photographer who had spent a good deal of his life in Rome. He had blond hair and blue eyes, and no one suspected he was French until he spoke; his accent was little altered despite ten years of living in New York. François considered himself very charming; it was impossible for him to meet a woman without a great show of hand kissing. He was also terribly egocentric, and could not be involved in any group activity without placing himself at the very center. He was Roman Catholic and fearfully superstitious as well. But he was a tremendous cook and most of the time a good companion.

Our house was a large, modern architect's house directly fronting the ocean. The bedrooms and dining room, one wall of which was the kitchen, had not walls, but partitions that could be folded open or shut, allowing the rooms to become part of the living area. There was plenty of space: Michael and François shared one bedroom, Howard and I the other—the one on the ocean side. In addition, there were in the living room two long

daybeds arranged in an L shape that could easily
sleep two, and often did. What with friends visiting from town, or neighbors coming in for dinner,
the house was usually full of people on weekends.
The entire front of the house was made of glass:
The living-room section had sliding doors that
gave onto a broad wooden deck, which was raised
like a mezzanine above the level of the beach. It
was larger than the one I had shared before and
with four of us the cost was reasonable. I had always liked this house architecturally, and furthermore, it was right on the ocean.

And the house had one more distinction. *It was
the same house to which I had been brought after
nearly drowning the summer before.*

It really was too cold to swim that evening, but
Howard and Michael went in anyway. François
and I went about setting up the house—making
up the beds, hooking up the stereo, putting the
records and books away, and getting the kitchen
organized. The kitchen was largely François's do-
main. And we were happy to have it so—he was a
fine cook. He had brought with him some home-
made pasta from a little Italian shop on Ninth
Avenue, and that evening he cooked it with fresh
ricotta cheese and a fantastic sauce of sautéed
but practically uncooked tomatoes, peppers,
onions, garlic, and fresh basil. We ate very well
that summer. There was not much drinking. Howard liked his gin and tonic, but usually he drank
those at the Boatel, where he often went to social-

ize. I loved wine with dinner. Michael and François drank hardly anything at all.

After dinner we all stayed at the round pine table full of coffee cups and wine glasses, unwilling to get up. All the activity and preparation over with, the summer suddenly seemed to begin, and we were relaxed and satisfied, enjoying the moment. The conversation drifted from topic to topic. There was a lot of laughing and a couple of aborted attempts to clear the table and do the dishes. The puppies were biting and chasing one another around the living-room floor. Someone suggested we go down to the Boatel, but that idea was not very appealing to me.

"You can go ahead if you want," I said, "but I think I'll stay here and read." I was reading *Rosemary's Baby*, the book of the hour. Howard was the only one who had read it. He thought the writing was good but the premise rather ridiculous. I agreed. Michael was very much interested in the occult and eager to read it. "Just because we see only three dimensions," he said, "doesn't mean that others don't exist." You couldn't have bribed François to read it. He was a fundamentalist, totally convinced of the existence of the netherworld, of devils, evil beings, and threatening spirits who could possess people and send them straight to eternal damnation.

"That's black magic," he said. "I'm not reading any books about it."

"Come off it," Howard said. He was the least

tolerant of François and the least credulous when it came to otherworldly things. He was concerned only with the here and now—his career and having a good time.

"True or not," Michael said, "I think there's something to this idea of linking up with the spirit world."

My mind was split on the subject. On the one hand, I didn't believe that Satan cults existed except in fiction and in tales about Salem and medieval Europe. On the other, I had always had a mild intellectual curiosity about such things as ESP and astrology. Still, I mistrusted it. "People become emotional," I said. "They make themselves believe in things that aren't really there. They use it to escape from reality. If people want to believe in anything badly enough, it can become real to them."

"I disagree," said Michael. "My grandmother has certain powers that cannot be explained in terms of three-dimensional reality. I can call her on the telephone and pick out playing cards one at a time, and she can tell me over the phone which cards I am holding. She's never wrong."

François, who had lived in Rome during his childhood, told us that black magic was still practiced there by colonies of witches—old men and women who wore long robes and held ceremonies in secret places. "They are not the only group in that city wearing long robes who appeal to the emotions and control others by use of fear," countered Howard.

"I'm talking about putting spells on people—witches who can cause harm and do evil things to you," said François, offended by Howard's reference.

"Well, I think the whole thing is a lot of hogwash," Howard said. "Real is real. Just because people imagine something does not make it suddenly spring to life."

François was becoming more and more irritated at Howard. "It is real, by God," he said angrily. "I remember, when I was a child, seeing old women carving little dolls out of wood, and dressing them with bits of fabric and thread and dyes. They would say incantations over them, casting spells on people, and sticking pins into the dolls to make someone become ill or even die. And people did die."

"Nonsense," said Howard. "Sticking pins into dolls doesn't do anything. They only think it does because they are superstitious and ignorant."

"But the spirit world does exist," said Michael calmly, intervening. "I've seen mediums at work many times. Most of them are fakes and easy to expose. But my grandmother knows one or two who could actually mediate between the physical world and the spirit world. It does exist."

I was fascinated. The only séances I'd ever seen were on television or in movies where the medium is exposed at the end as a clever fake and usually the perpetrator of some cunning crime. As far as I knew, séances were invented as plot devices by mystery writers. The idea that actual, sane people participated in them for the purpose of contacting the dead was one that had never presented itself to me as a viable possibility. However, my Episcopalian upbringing had taught me that life continued after death, and I believed it. I said it seemed to me that if one could make contact with someone who had died, this would be strong evidence of an afterlife.

"Why don't we try it ourselves, right now?" Michael suggested.

"Try what?" I asked.

"Contacting the spirit world," he said matter-of-factly.

I leaned forward. "How could we do it? Do you think you could actually conduct a séance yourself?"

Michael had never been to a séance himself, but he said he knew how to use a Ouija board.

"They are the instruments of evil spirits who want to take over your soul," said François. "I've seen people go into trances where they cannot move or speak. Don't do it. It's dangerous."

I looked at him, then at Howard. Howard was leaning back in his chair; he said nothing.

"Come on, François," I said. "Let's try it."

Michael got a Magic Marker from his room, while I cleared the rest of the things from the table. François reluctantly helped clean up the kitchen. I took the puppies out for a few minutes, then put them to bed for the night on a blanket in the large bathroom behind the kitchen.

Michael took the black marker and drew on the

surface of the round pine dining table. He made a circle of letters—all the letters in the alphabet, evenly spaced on a diameter of about eighteen inches. Across the diameter he wrote the numbers 1 2 3 4 5 6 7 8 9 0, and below them, also inside the circle of letters, YES and NO.

"We'll need something to write on if the board tells us anything," he said, so I fetched a legal pad from my suitcase. Michael rummaged through the kitchen cupboard for a tumbler or glass to use as a marker. One glass was much too thick and heavy, another too tall. The stemmed goblets were too fragile and toppled easily. He settled on a small, lightweight juice glass that slid easily across the surface of the table. It hitched at a couple of rough places, so Michael lightly smoothed these with olive oil. Last, he placed the glass, inverted, in the very center of the home-made Ouija.

François grew more and more agitated. "You're out of your minds to meddle with this," he ranted.

If it hadn't been for François's histrionics, I think Howard would have gone out or to bed. I'm sure he thought François was too ridiculous to be taken seriously, and I suspect he agreed to participate just for spite, since he assured us the whole thing was sheer nonsense. That left François with a choice: He could join us, or he could go out by himself, or he could go to bed. He was much too egocentric to go out while the rest of the group was involved in something; above all he needed to be included. He sat down at the table.

"What now?" I asked. Michael told Howard to turn the light down; he reached for the dimmer that controlled the huge black wrought-iron chandelier above our heads and reduced the light to practically nothing. Michael had turned out all the living-room lamps. But even that wasn't good enough. Michael said there had to be a certain atmosphere for this to have any chance at all. It had to be quiet and dark, and we had to keep our minds calm and receptive.

I went to the kitchen and rummaged through the drawers for a candle. I found one, but since there was no candle holder, I had to make one by dripping some wax into a big heavy glass ashtray. I stuck the candle into the hot wax and placed it on the table between Michael and Howard. When the chandelier was switched off completely, the solitary candle became the only light in the house.

I could feel a definite excitement, a kind of uneasiness that made us all a bit apprehensive. We looked at each other, not knowing exactly what to do. Michael took a breath, reached out and put his finger on the perimeter of the inverted glass. I followed suit, then Howard did the same. François hesitated, looking at us one by one. When his eyes reached mine I could see the real fear there. He paused uncertainly, then stretched his finger toward the glass, and made contact.

Nothing happened.

We sat there for a few minutes. In a quiet voice, Michael told us that we should clear our minds, to forget everything except this contact, this feeling of the glass touching our fingers. We concentrated. Nothing happened.

I suggested that perhaps an invocation of some kind was necessary. Nobody had any better suggestions, so I went out to the living room. The curtains were drawn but the sliding glass doors behind them were wide open. I parted the curtains with my hands and walked through to the deck. I stood quietly listening to the sound of the breakers. Apart from that sound, the night was still. The air was calm, and the sky clear and filled with stars. I felt very self-conscious and slightly nervous. I decided that, if we were going to attempt this experiment, I was going to give it a fair chance. But I had no idea what I was doing. I thought for a moment, then I said, aloud so the others could hear me inside:

"If there is any spirit, anyone here who wants to communicate with us, we welcome you. We don't want to harm you, and we don't want to be harmed. If we can help in any way, please come and make contact with us." I stood quietly for a moment more. Then I realized I was dead serious.

I walked back inside, silently and with deliberation. Everyone was quiet. Suddenly the curtain billowed out with an unexpected wind, and the two dogs in the back room began a low, eerie growling sound. The four of us touched our fingers to the edge of the glass. Incredibly, the glass started to move around the circle of letters rapidly, never pausing. It spun around the alphabet and back and forth across the numbers, uncontrolled and extremely fast. We had to struggle to keep up with it.

Howard immediately suspected someone of pushing the glass. Could he be right? I couldn't believe Michael or François could push the glass so fast, so deftly. It raced around the table and couldn't seem to stop. It was as if we were not attached to our fingers.

"Why doesn't it stop?" François said in a strange voice.

"Maybe there's too much energy," Michael said. "Maybe the four of us are too many." Howard took his finger off and the glass slowed. He made it clear that he accepted none of this nonsense. The glass was still moving fast around the circle of letters, back and forth across the numbers. It seemed to be investigating the board. The rest of us kept our fingers touching. The energy was palpable. I could feel it clearly; Michael seemed to be almost mesmerized, very quiet and intense, focused on the glass.

Howard suggested we ask a question. I looked at Michael, but he was preoccupied. I considered for a moment.

"Whom do you want to speak to?" I asked aloud.

The glass moved rapidly from letter to letter. François and I said the letters out loud as the glass hit them. Howard grabbed the pad and began to write. It took a few seconds for him to divide the letters into words. Michael was absolutely silent.

ALL CONCERNED

Howard read it derisively. "Very good," he said. I suppose he was still convinced that someone was pushing the glass. But it would have been impossible unless the three of us had staged and rehearsed it. The glass proceeded from letter to letter so fast that just keeping up with it required intense concentration. I was dumbfounded at what was happening. Michael was useless, lost in concentration. François quivered with fear. I realized it was up to me.

"Who are you?" I asked. The glass responded.

ZENA

"What do you want to say?" Howard wrote furiously as the glass flew from letter to letter, François and I calling them out as they were touched. The glass came smoothly to rest at the center, and the energy stopped. We waited anxiously for Howard to divide the jumble of letters into words.

VERY UNUSUAL TO BE AS LONELY SO LONG BY MYSELF REST FOR TEN

"We are not sure what you mean," I began. But the energy had stopped, and the glass did not move.

We were speechless. Where did the words come from? What was this? The four of us looked at one another, full of questioning. "To be as lonely . . ." What did it mean? And "Rest for ten"?

"It meant," Howard assured us, "that it will

take ten minutes for whoever is pushing that glass to get the game going again." We all looked at him.

"Well, I wasn't pushing it," said François.

"Nor was I," I said.

"No one was," Michael said. "The energy that moved that glass came from something in this room, not from us—and so did the messages."

I didn't know what to think. Could Michael actually be staging this somehow?

We all wanted to hear the messages again, and Howard read the messages aloud. None of it made much sense. Zena. Was that a name? It was impossible to think clearly.

Before ten minutes was up, I placed my finger on the edge of the glass, anxious to continue. François and Michael did the same. Instantly the glass began to move. This time it did not wait for a question, but sped from letter to letter immediately. There was no way to decipher the message as it was being given—the glass went too fast. When it rested at the center, Howard went back and made sense of the jumble.

RED NIGHT NO HELP FOR ME

François's attitude toward the Ouija changed conspicuously and inexplicably. Seeing that a contact had apparently been made, and that none of us was mad or catatonic, he leaped to the center of attention.

"Wait!" he exclaimed, flushed with excitement. "Shall I become rich and famous as a photographer?"

The glass moved to NO. Incredulous, I shot François a look. What was he doing?

"Will I have my contract with *Vogue*?" he persisted.

"François, shut up," I said.

The glass moved: YES. And then ALONE YES

I was not about to let François's ego interfere with my getting to the bottom of this phenomenon. I had no idea what could be controlling the glass, but I seemed to be the only one interested in finding out.

"When did you die?" I asked.

1873

"Where did you come from?"

LIVERPOOL I FELT NO PAIN

"When will my success begin?" François interrupted, fairly shouting. I couldn't believe he was doing this. The glass moved. Howard wrote, then read the reply:

PLEASE LET ME BE IN CONTACT

"François, quit it," I told him, glaring. "Look at the information we're getting." I wondered if we could document any of this. The glass moved.

NO NEED

"Do you want to speak to all?"

YES

François couldn't contain himself. "Will you speak to me, spirit?" The glass did not move. "Will you tell me what you want?"

NO

"Will you tell the others?" No answer.

"Will you tell Michael?" I asked.

YES NIGHT I NEED TIME TO JUST BE PATIENT
Howard read as he deciphered.

"Are you from New York?" I asked. A test
question, trying for inconsistencies.

NO

"What do you want?" A rush of energy as the
glass touched letter after letter. Howard worked
on it a moment, then read:

TO TELL YOU ZENA NOT ALWAYS

"What does that mean?" I looked at Michael.
His eyes were transfixed on the board. Perspiration was beading across his hairline.

"Where were you born?"

LIVERPOOL

"Are you a woman?"

YES

"Are you unhappy?"

YES

"How can we help you?" Again the glass
touched the letters, crisscrossing the circle with
phenomenal speed. And then it came to rest at the
center of the circle. The energy ceased. I could
feel its sudden absence as clearly as if someone
had switched off some strange current.

"What did it say?" I asked Howard, who was
still decoding. He looked up.

BE TOGETHER IN TIME

Michael seemed to be released when the energy
flow stopped. The three of us sat for nearly half
an hour longer, trying to get some further response—asking questions, concentrating with all
our strength. But whatever it was, it was over.

When we accepted that, we also realized that we were utterly exhausted.

No one had any reasonable explanation for what had happened, and we were too stunned to think about it much. Howard was not so sure of himself as when we had begun, but he maintained that there was some logical explanation for everything that had happened.

François began complaining again. I couldn't believe it—after his outrageous and childish behavior during the episode. I was very irritated with him, but said nothing.

Michael was exhilarated and, although physically exhausted from the strain, seemed curiously refreshed and pleased by the experience.

I felt no emotions either negative or positive. All I knew for sure was that I had felt some other presence in the room, and a strange energy. There was no rational way to explain such a thing. And now that it was over, I was struck by its total implausibility. How could I believe that a being from an unseen world, a dead spirit, had contacted us through a circle of letters and a glass. It couldn't be. And yet, there had been an unmistakable energy. I knew I had felt it, and I knew I had seen the juice glass spin out messages all by itself. "And the dogs—they growled when the wind blew the curtains," I reminded everyone. "Whatever it was, they felt it, too."

By this time it was nearly two A.M., and we knew we had to get some rest. I forced myself through the rituals, totally preoccupied, and got into bed. I could see the blackness of the sky beyond the window. But my head was full, my eyes would not close, and it was a long time before I could unwind and go to sleep.

SECOND ENCOUNTER

Saturday, July 1

By the time I got up the next morning, the sun was already high, and the others had breakfasted and were out on the beach. I fixed myself some fruit and coffee and joined them. I was still very much under the influence of the morning's last dream—in fact, all that had happened the night before seemed very unreal and dreamlike. Yet I knew it was real: It had happened not to just one of us, but to us all; we had witnessed it together. And for some reason, now, after a night's sleep, and with the sun shining brilliantly on a beach dotted with weekenders, the events of the past evening, instead of assuming more sensible proportions, seemed even more staggering.

People would stroll up the beach and sit in the sand to visit with us for a while. They would strike up conversations, and we would smile and try to be sociable. But it wasn't working. The people would drift away again. We all knew what we really wanted to talk about.

Michael was the first to bring up the subject. He couldn't wait. When could we try again to contact the spirit? François's reaction was predictable: Never again would he have anything to do with it. He would not risk incurring the wrath of God.

Howard thought we were all deluding ourselves. He granted that maybe we weren't consciously pushing the glass, but insisted that something somewhere in our unconscious certainly was in control. He accused us of wanting so badly for the Ouija to work that we had convinced ourselves we had actually contacted spirits. According to Howard, the entire episode was self-induced and self-fulfilling. I could see that he had a point. In fact, I myself had said much the same thing before we had begun the night before: If you want to believe in something hard enough, you can almost will it to happen.

While maintaining his belief that we had indeed contacted the spirit of a dead person, Michael had another theory: The glass, he said, might be a focalization point of all the energy in the room—our own psychic energy, not spirit energy. The messages that appeared to be coming from some force outside ourselves might actually have been the product of one of our imaginations, probably that of the strongest-willed of the group. I found the hypothesis interesting, largely because it raised another question: Which of us could be the source of such communication? Who was the person with such a vivid imagination that his unconscious could spin off a yarn like that, creating a character from some other time?

Michael proposed that perhaps the woman Zena was not imaginary, but a memory of some other lifetime that one of us had once lived. Howard thought the whole thing was too farfetched for words. "It's just a parlor game," he said, "and it's not what I came out here for."

"Well, I think we should try it again," said Michael. "We made contact once. I'd like to see if we can do it a second time. Imagine really communicating with the spirit world."

"Imagine," said François importantly, "and imagine how it would be for them to take over our souls. I am not going to give them another chance."

I still had some questions about all this. To begin with, the whole idea of a spirit world was something out of fiction. To make the transition to reality was not easy. I didn't know for sure whether spirits really existed in the first place. And if they really did, how could we know whether they were benign or malevolent? But I was curious enough—or perhaps ignorant enough—to be sure of one thing: If we could learn more about it, I wanted the chance to do so. I don't know why it never occurred to us to try it right then. Certainly at least Michael and I were eager enough. We just never thought about it. Matters of this nature seemed more appropriate at night, when the world was still and dark. During the day, it might be difficult to establish the proper atmosphere or the mood necessary for concentration. Then too, there was the fear that we might be interrupted, and we did not want to be discovered. At least I didn't.

"We shouldn't tell anyone about this," I said. "People will think we're crazy." So we made a pact to keep the episode to ourselves, at least until we knew more about what we were actually dealing with.

Michael and I had a little trouble later on, convincing Howard and François that we ought to have another go at the Ouija that night. Howard couldn't have acted more blasé, but I had a feeling he would be around to watch the proceedings, if only to laugh at us in the event we could not recall the spirit to the table. He might have put down the idea, but he was curious too. François was no problem. He ranted and raved about the Devil, but I knew that although he was very superstitious, he was also incapable of leaving the house knowing that something exciting might be taking place. He was all bravura and bravado but had the least self-confidence of any of us. He manufactured an identity for himself by overdramatizing everything that happened to him: every little illness, every imagined slight or insult, every foreboding. It didn't take much to get him to go along: All one had to do was to flatter him. He wasn't stupid, and in fact was very shrewd, but weakened by his vanity and his ambition. We knew he would be with us that night.

After dinner Michael touched up the letters and numbers on the Ouija board and oiled a few rough spots on the bare pine wood to make sure the glass would glide easily. I helped François clear the table and put the puppies to bed in the back room. Howard got a pencil and the yellow pad and sat down at the table to wait.

When everyone was ready, I lit the candle and turned out the light. We sat down, composed ourselves for a moment in the darkness, and put our fingers on the upturned bottom of the glass.

"Well, do you think we should begin?" I asked. "Shall we call Zena?" Immediately the glass moved smoothly to YES. We looked at one another in surprise. There had not even been an invocation tonight; apparently the spirits were already there. Or someone—Michael was the logical choice —actually was controlling the glass. I decided to watch very carefully. If he was doing it unconsciously, perhaps I would be able to detect it.

"Tell us your story," I said to the glass. Howard recorded as François and I again called off the letters. I was amazed at its speed and smoothness. There was no hesitation whatever. While Howard was figuring it out, I glanced at Michael. He was sitting absolutely straight and still, his eyes fixed, his finger motionless on the glass. He seemed to be exerting no effort whatever. It was as if his body were there, but his mind elsewhere, cap-tured.

Howard read:

YOU ARE GOING TO ASK LIES

Riddles, I thought. I'd better ask more specific questions.

"Will you tell me what you want us to know?" I asked.

YES

"Why won't you answer others who ask?" Our fingers struggled to keep up with the glass as it leaped from letter to letter, zigzagging across the alphabet circle. There was a delay while Howard decoded everything. The glass was stationary at the center, at rest. I looked steadily at François, and he at me. The message was lengthy.

BECAUSE YOU SHOULD NOT ASK IN FRONT OF OTHER There was a pause. MY CHILD

"Is your child here now?" I asked.

NO

"Is your child's spirit present?"

YES

"Here now?"

YES

"What can we do?" There was no answer. François began to fidget. I spoke quickly. "Is there someone here besides you?"

YES MICHAEL FRANCOIS HOWARD YOU

We did not need to wait for Howard to write. We recognized our names as they were spelled. I shuddered involuntarily. It was a disquieting thought that the spirit knew our names. And that it seemed to be addressing me. Unless . . . I glanced at Michael. He seemed totally engrossed.

"Me?" I asked.

YOU KNOW

I stopped and shook my head to try to clear it. I was having a conversation with—something. I did not know how to go on. I looked at the faces around the table. Silent faces, one completely absorbed, another just as completely uninvolved, the third growing more nervous by the minute.

"Is there no one to help you?" I asked, groping.

YES I HELP YOU

"She can help?" François asked. "Can you help me, spirit?"

Howard looked up at François and was about to say something, but I interrupted. I knew that ordering him to stop asking personal questions would only cause a scene, which I wanted to avoid. The only way to handle François was to make it worth his while to be quiet.

"If we block the messages by asking unrelated questions," I explained in a hushed, serious voice, "we won't get any information from the spirit. Let's find out what we're dealing with first. If it's valuable to us, we can get all the personal information we want later on." François seemed to see the point. I tried to focus my attention back on the Ouija.

"How can you help?" I asked.

NO QUESTIONS

Howard wrote down the messages, but these shorter transmissions were becoming easy for us to read as they were given. It was as if the Ouija had its own silent language, which we were already beginning to understand. The letters formed themselves into words for us.

"Shall we continue?" I asked the group. The men hesitated—but the glass responded:

YES

Startled, I groped for a question.

"What is your child's name?"

YOU KNOW

"We don't know."

YES

"Do you mean I am your child?" A nonsensical question. The spirit wasn't making any sense.

NO

"Is your child here in this room?" There was no answer. The glass stood still in the center of the table. But the energy was still there. I could still feel that it had not stopped. "Do you want your child?"

YES 1873 YES

"Was your child lost in 1873 also?"

YES

"Was your child lost near here?"

YES

"Was its spirit lost too?"

NO

"Are you looking for your child?"

We looked at Howard, waiting for him to decipher the answer.

YES HIGGINS HOME

"Your child's spirit is at Higgins's home?" (Who was Higgins?)

YES

"Is it there now?"

YES

"Is your child a girl?"

YES

"Is she beautiful?" François asked. Howard shut him up with a sharp glance. He wrote the letters as we called out:

SHE IS MY LIE   A pause, then   CHAINED HER AWAY

"Who has chained her away? Higgins?" I asked.

THE WORLD WATER

"Is he an evil man?"

YES

"Is his spirit here?" I was beginning to feel uneasy. But I kept on.

YES

"Has he got your child?"

YES

"How old is she?"

12

"Where is her father?" The glass did not move. There was a long pause, and I felt the energy weaken and almost fade out. I took my finger off the glass experimentally and replaced it. The sensation was still there. The energy was still flowing, but weakly. Michael seemed to be back with us now. I had not been thinking very much about Michael; I was so involved in learning Zena's story, whoever Zena was. I was feeling strong human emotions. This woman had lost and was searching for her child, kidnapped by someone named Higgins. It was like hearing the story of a living person, and I felt myself very much inexplicably wanting to help. And yet, intellectually, I was still suspicious. I refused to let myself be duped by something that might turn out to be a trick. I was torn between my natural inclination to believe and my natural reservations. The result was confusion. No one spoke during this long pause. We knew it was not yet over. Suddenly the energy flowed strongly again, like a water tap turned on full force. The glass moved:

ALWAYS PROTECTED

"Do you know about us?" I asked. What else could the message writer tell us about ourselves? Was there something about myself that Michael would not know, that I could ask as a test?

NO

But she knew our names. Were spirits able to read minds or weren't they? Questions unanswered.

"Where did you come from?" I had asked it before, but the question just came out. I didn't know what to do next. I couldn't think. And there was no help forthcoming from any of the others. The glass sped around the board; Howard took down the reply.

MY GRAVE UNDER THE SEA

"In the sea?"

YES

"Is it near us now?"

YES ALL ALONE

"Do you have a daughter?"

NO SHE IS CHILD OF MY SISTER BETH

A shock. That was what she had meant when she said her child was her lie.

"What is her name?" I asked.

ROSAMOND BROOKE

"And your sister is Beth?"

YES SHE WILL TRY TO TAKE MY PLACE SHE IS EVIL SHE CANNOT BE TRUSTED

It took a few seconds for Howard to figure out this long message. And more for us to digest it.

"Did she die with you in 1873?" We waited impatiently for the reply. Howard read:

NO LATER SHE AND HIGGINS DROWNED IN SEA

"By accident?"

YES IN A BOAT DROWNED

"Near here?"

AT WATER ISLAND WHERE THEY LIVED There was a pause, then BOOK RED AND GREEN A pause. VERY COLD OBLIVION SEALED IN COLD

"You mean the water in your grave is cold?"

OUT HERE AS THEN A pause. LOGS RECORDS LIVERPOOL LOG RED NIGHT DEEP INSIDE ARNOLD HOWARD FRANCOIS MICHAEL VERY PATIENT MY NEW PEOPLE

It sounded as if she was going to leave us. I searched for the question that would make her continue. "Will you be with us all night?"

ALWAYS UNTIL BOOK RED ASSURES YOU A pause. BY THE LARGE HILL TODAY READ OF LOG RED NIGHT Pause. OBLIVION

A shiver crept up my neck. "You mean oblivion for you? Not for us?"

ONE I HELP   CATTLE FOR PEOPLE DEEP   WE WERE DEEP INSIDE LIKE CATTLE

"You mean you were treated like cattle on the ship?"

YES GOODBYE

And the energy switched off. She was gone. We sat there for a moment, not moving. I looked at Michael; he was no longer in a trancelike state. Where had he been during the séance? Was he a medium—or a practical joker? The candle had burned to a short stump. Howard reached over to switch on the overhead light; we all blinked against the sudden brightness. François went to put on some water in the kitchen, not because anyone wanted coffee as much as for something to do. My own head was reeling. "Let's hear again what the spirit said," I suggested. "Maybe we can figure something out." Howard read us his scrawly transcript. A story was definitely unfolding. Zena and Rosamond Brooke had died at sea. Rosamond was her niece, but for some reason she was under Zena's care. And Zena referred to her as her child although she really was her sister Beth's child. Zena must have been traveling from England in steerage: "Deep inside like cattle." And she was trying to get us to do something: "Red night. Logs records. Book red and green. By the large hill." What did it all mean? And who was Higgins? Whoever he was, he and Beth must have lived together at the time of their death. And in Water Island, the tiny, remote community about half an hour's walk east from our house.

"Do you still think one of us is making up this story?" I asked Howard. He said he still did think so, but to me his tone of voice didn't sound so sure anymore. I thought about it myself: a story from the unconscious? A memory from a past life? And if not from Michael, could the story be mine? Somehow it just didn't ring true. I had been participating in a conversation with something, but on what I felt was a very human level: I did not feel deeply, intuitively involved. François was out of the question as a source of such a tale. I doubted that he was able to concentrate enough even to add much energy to the operation. He was far too involved with himself. But Michael—Michael was a real possibility. He was totally absorbed in the proceedings, and he never said a word. And there was other evidence: his interest in the occult, and his heredity, his grandmother, who received visual messages over the telephone. But when I brought myself to suggest it, he assured me that none of the story rang so much as a distant bell for him—that had all been a theory, possibilities, conjecture. In view of what happened tonight, Michael said he was convinced there was an actual Zena, the spirit of a human Zena who had died a hundred years before, making contact with us by some invisible and incomprehensible means.

I felt suddenly drained; my head could hold no more tonight. I stood up and took a deep breath. "Good night, gentlemen," I said.

I was awakened Sunday morning by the sounds of Joshua and Rachel romping on the beach outside my open window. Someone had apparently let them out. The ocean breeze wafted warmly across my bed. I got up, pulled on my trunks, and walked out onto the deck. In early morning light, the pale hazy colors of the sea and sky seemed to blend together in an allover silver-mauve watercolor, with lavender clouds hanging low over the distant horizon. The tide was out, and in the distance a dark piling of some sort protruded above the surface of the water. A few birds skimmed along the waveless shore, surface fishing. Gulls reeled and called overhead. I breathed deeply, trying to hold this beautiful image in my mind. But it was rapidly taken over by memories of the past two nights. And of last night in particular.

53

Later, when the four of us were lying in the
sun on the beach, we talked more about Zena's
story and the strange clues that had been strewn
seemingly haphazardly throughout the messages.
And the riddles. What was "red night"? The name
of a ship? Or could she have meant there was a
fire? Why didn't she say so? Why must she speak
in riddles? Well, if the information we had received contained any truth, perhaps a little research would give us more facts. I decided to
make a trip to the library during the week. "Book.
Logs records," Zena had said. What was she trying to tell us?"

I expected a reaction from Michael, but it was
François's response to my plans to go to the
library that came as a surprise. He tried to per-
suade me not to do it. What could he be afraid
of? Maybe that we would learn something? Maybe he was afraid there actually was a shipwreck
in 1873, and some of Zena's information would
fit. Then his deeper fears would suddenly be sup-
ported: We would have documentation that there
were living beings in another world. François
would like to stay clear of mysticism—leave that
sort of thing to the Church. But even if I could
find some written proof, who would believe our
story?

That night we all drove back to town together.
There was room in the car for the four of us,
since most of what we had brought out was staying at the house. But the drive seemed very long
and very tiring. The roads were clogged with end-

less weekend traffic, and after all we had been through, the drive seemed doubly exhausting. I dropped everyone off at his own apartment, drove the car to the garage, and was grateful to get home, where I could finally release the two restless puppies. I was mentally exhausted. I fell into bed, slept heavily, and woke still tired after a night of vivid dreams.

Weekdays were usually working days for me, but I couldn't wait to get to the bottom of Zena's story. I canceled all my appointments and headed for the New York Public Library, where I hoped to find an answer or even a clue to this extraordinary story. I was very excited as I mounted the tiers of stone steps to the monumental Beaux Arts building guarded by its two famous lions. Inside, my footsteps resounded as I climbed more marble stairs to the third floor and the American history rooms. I was familiar with this part of the library; I loved research and history, and frequently came here to pore over old records in search of obscure information.

The librarian, a kind-faced man who recognized me from my past visits, was happy to assist me with information as to which books possibly contained any information that listed the names and dates of shipwrecks around the waters of Long Island. I was staggered by the number. There must have been dozens of books—and each book listed innumerable wrecks. I searched through file cards and filled out white call slips, which I then exchanged for an enormous stack of books. I carried them to one of the long wooden tables among the book stacks. Around me were scatterings of people silently engrossed in research. The atmosphere was hushed, the only sound that of pages slowly turning. It occurred to me that the library was a kind of tomb containing fragments of records from past times. Like a museum, lifeless.

I began by digging through old newspaper files for Long Island, bound copies of small local newspapers. Shipwrecks were indexed under "Shipwrecks—see Disasters." I searched through the old record books that listed every shipwreck by name of ship, date of wreck, captain, home port, destination, number of persons on board, and how the wreck occurred. There were many indexed under Long Island, and a great many of these occurred off Fire Island. This is where I concentrated my research.

I spent all day Monday in the library without success. I went home and caught up on some paperwork for my business, staying up far into the night. I knew I had to get back to the library the next day.

On Wednesday I found something. Not anything I could be sure of, but in the *Long Island Forum* were listed many shipwrecks off Long Island and in particular off Fire Island during the winter of 1872–1873. This was the only date given for any serious sea disasters in that area with the exception of a few isolated incidents prior to that date. There were several articles in several volumes, and they all reiterated the fact that this was the worst winter on record and described the dense fogs which closed in over Fire Island and made it impossible to see the shoreline or the lighthouses. Innumerable wrecks occurred along the entire stretch of Long Island. Fire Island beach was strewn with wreckage and more than one human body was found on the shore. Not all the ships seemed to have been victims of storms or darkness. One article told how many ships were lured to destruction by wreckers, who lit signal fires to guide ships onto shoals and reefs: "The fewer survivors the better, as far as these bloodthirsty men were concerned."

It seemed so odd that this was the only year cited in all the volumes during the nineteenth century, except for those few others and they were all much earlier. Nothing else was listed until after the turn of the century.

When I got back from the library, I called my three housemates on the telephone and told them what I had discovered. Howard thought it was the slightest straw to grasp at and did not consider it valid evidence. Michael was instantly convinced that one of these was indeed the very wreck. And François, who was convinced anyway that the spirits were real, only became more negative.

"Stay away from anything that has to do with ghosts and spirits," he said. "If it happened, it happened a hundred years ago. And no one knew until you invited the spirits in. It's none of our business, not for us to know."

The next day I received a call from François, very agitated. He told me he would not be coming out to the house that weekend because he had too much work to do, but I knew it was the good chance that we might try another séance that upset him. I felt rather ashamed, because François was, after all, paying a fourth of the rent, and he was entitled to a pleasant weekend as much as any of us. Reluctantly, I told him that we would not get involved with the Ouija that weekend and assured him I would convince the others. He seemed mollified and agreed to come out.

Michael was the only one who needed convincing, since Howard could take it or leave it anyway. I telephoned Michael and we discussed not taking it any further. For François's sake, and to keep the peace. And it probably was best not to go too far with the thing anyway. We succeeded in convincing ourselves, and decided to give it up.

Aside from that, Thursday was an ordinary workday, busy and rather mundane. My fascination with the spiritual actually left me, forgotten in the distractions of the real world.

But on Friday, when Michael and François and I were driving back to the ferry that would take us to the beach house, the magic lure began to arouse us again. Michael and I rehashed my research and reminded one another of clues Zena had given us. In town, the whole thing had seemed somehow distant and removed, and it had been easy to agree not to go ahead. But now our curi-

osity was building again. And there was no Howard with us to balance our enthusiasm with his
cool, down-to-earth skepticism. François, sitting
in the back seat, leaned forward, closer and closer
as we talked, becoming more and more worried,
reminding us again and again of our agreement.
I couldn't help but feel guilty about François's
plight; I knew how really distressed he was and I
recognized that he deserved to have a summer
house he could relax in and enjoy. But more
strongly than guilt I felt an urge I could not deny,
the urge to find out more. At last even François
realized there was no hope of dissuading us. We
had to try again.

THIRD ENCOUNTER

Friday, July 7

When the three of us arrived at the house, we found Howard already there, having arrived earlier by train. The stereo in the house was blaring Bob Dylan, but Howard, wearing swim trunks and a sweater, was out on the beach, propped up against a beach chair, reading a book. His hair was wet from swimming. Howard loved the water. He had spent his childhood in Connecticut on Long Island Sound. He was quickly tanning, which looked terrific with his sunstreaked hair. He was definitely Ivy League stock, tall, with a winning, quiet personality, and what some women called bedroom eyes.

There was still time for a swim before sunset. The air was cool, but the drive had been so hot and stuffy that I wanted at least to get wet. Swimming in the ocean off Long Island at the beginning of July was, except for the heartiest, a matter of rushing in, splashing briefly until the shock of the sudden cold wore off, and running out again into a warm towel. The two puppies were beginning to like the water. They would play on the beach, chasing one another, their paws and stomachs and long ears dipping into the shallow surf. If a wave came, they would scamper up the beach out of its reach. The puppies were a pleasure to me that summer.

François had brought some homemade pasta and fresh herbs for dinner, and, since everyone seemed to be starving, he began preparing dinner earlier than usual. We were joined for the weekend by a girlfriend of mine, Sharma, a well-known ballerina, who arrived on a later ferry. She was from Ceylon and possessed an extraordinary Anglo-Eastern beauty. Her skin was dark olive, and her shining, jet-black hair was brushed thickly back from her beautiful smooth forehead to fall in waves down her back. Her eyes were dark and rimmed with long lashes, and in the center of her forehead she often painted a red dot. She wore saris—not always, but a good deal of the time. (Some of my friends thought it was an affectation.) François and Sharma did not especially get along, but they both made an effort for the sake of harmony. She was a tough woman under a surface of very soft little-girl manners which could sometimes admittedly become irritating. But she was extremely charming and a fascinating conversationalist who spoke with a pleasant Oxford accent acquired during her dance training in England. With her was her small terrier, Tiger, who was never more than a few steps from Sharma, no matter where she went. She even took Tiger to restaurants and kept him hidden under her sari.

I am certain part of François's hostility toward her had to do with jealousy and his own insecurity. He knew that she could see right through him. It was Sharma who had told me she thought François was gay and all that bravado was a mask to conceal his secret. Also, Sharma stole some of François's limelight; she too was an excellent cook.

Neither Michael nor I said a word about the séances past, nor any we hoped to have in the future. But that did not mean we weren't thinking about it. In fact, I could think of very little else. But I did not want it to appear that I was forcing the issue. I knew that Sharma was well versed in dealings with the spirit world, having been raised in a country where spirits are considered just another form of life—to be accepted, respected, and not worried much about. I learned that Ceylon is a country of many mysteries, including rituals of fire walking, where men and women, prepared only by three months of vegetarianism, daily baptisms in a holy river, and meditation, walk barefoot across a pit of coals smoldering at 450°C. at the surface, 1400°C. deep in the pit. These fire walkers sustain not so much as a blister, though a heedless and drunken tourist one year burned to an ash.

At the proper moment, I began asking Sharma about her background, which I already knew but thought the others might find interesting. And I knew her fascinating stories from childhood might rekindle Howard's and perhaps even François's interest in the Ouija.

Sharma was of mixed heritage—Dutch, English, and Sinhalese. She was raised by Roman Catholic parents—her father a philosopher and a poet, her mother a concert pianist. She was very well educated by any standard. Her Western ways were sophisticated, but her Eastern ones wise.

Sharma told us that when she was born, as when all children of certain castes are born in India, Ceylon, and neighboring regions, there was in attendance, besides the doctor and an assisting nurse, an astrologer. At the moment of Sharma's birth, an astrological chart was drawn and given to her parents, who, even though they were Catholics, were expected to nurture and understand the child according to her best auspices rather than their personal ambitions or desires. At home, a nonpoisonous snake was always kept in the house, to protect the family against the intrusion of malevolent spirits from the otherworld. That there was in fact an afterlife was something she never questioned, but Sharma also believed in the reincarnation of the spirit, and in karma: the personal fate which in Eastern thought we each weave for ourselves through successive lifetimes of deeds, misdeeds, and learning. The Christian religion teaches much the same thing: "As ye sow, so shall ye reap," but the phrase has been interpreted—perhaps erroneously, Sharma pointed out —to describe cause and effect in one lifetime rather than extending over many lifetimes. And that, she said, is why there appears to be so much injustice in the world, so much cruelty and selfishness going unpunished. Sharma had no doubt that perpetrators of sins against their fellow man, whether right or wrong by legal standards, would be dealt with in some future lifetime by a punishment that would exactly fit the crime.

Sharma's conversation was interesting and revealing. I was particularly curious about her thoughts on reincarnation, since it had been brought up the week before that perhaps Zena's story was true, but was being spun out of a past lifetime that one of us had lived, through some mysterious means none of us understood. I had, in fact, brought with me a book on reincarnation, which I intended to read on the beach the next day.

When I told Sharma that we had been involved in Ouija séances, she had surprisingly little reaction. She was well informed on the activities of mediums and the spirit world, but did not seem to be interested in dealing with spirits herself. If we were going to hold a séance, she would watch, but did not care to be involved.

"Why not?" Michael wanted to know.

It was like looking at a huge cobra coiled in a basket, she explained. She knew that the music of the flute would somehow make the cobra rise and sway. She did not know how. But she also knew that the cobra, once aroused, might get out of control. He might strike. The metaphor was all too clear.

"Why do you want to continue with your spirits?" Sharma asked. "What do you think you will gain?"

"Knowledge," I said. But Sharma did not think we would learn anything.

"Holy men can deal with the spirit world," she told us. "Men who are especially gifted, and who train for lifetimes, undergoing the most rigorous self-discipline. Those who know how to contact higher beings who really do have knowledge to give to help mankind." The most we could expect, she told us, was to contact the very low spirits of departed souls in what she called the astral plane, the dense region around the earth where lost and restless souls existed.

"These souls became lost," Sharma said, "because of their karmas, because of the way they lived, or the way they died." And the way they died depended on the way they lived in other lifetimes. The astral plane is full of the unsavory of humanity: criminals, people who were put to death—or who had others put to death. People who committed suicide, or who suffered violent deaths. People who had abnormal appetites of any kind, who craved cruelty or had other obsessions that threw them radically off balance. "A violent death," she explained, "cheats one of a completed

66

life. And so these souls are desperately looking for living people to attach themselves to, to feed on and use to prolong their own miserable lives." Sharma said matter-of-factly that even if we had succeeded in contacting beings from another plane, it could gain us nothing, and furthermore it was not something to be dealt with lightly.

The more she talked, however, the more excited I became. Regardless of where the spirits might have come from, the very fact that we might actually be contacting real spirits was a heady thought. And if these spirits were merely departed human beings, whom I certainly could handle if I met in physical form on the street, I was sure I was strong enough to withstand any onslaught from a being who needed a body for some miserable reasons of his or her own. Michael was beside himself with anticipation. François, siding with Sharma for once, made a strong appeal that we not try to contact Zena again. I was sure it was because he was so superstitious. Howard, on the other hand, seemed to be taking a real interest in the conversation tonight. There was nothing to do now but begin.

François and I cleared the table of platters and food. Sharma had not noticed the Ouija markings on the bare pine surface before.

"Really, you should at least keep the table covered when you're not using the Ouija," she said when she saw the board. "Leaving it exposed will attract all these beings like flies to honey." She told us that although we might think we were communicating with only one spirit, there might be literally hundreds in the room with us at this very moment. Spirits take up no space as we understand space. "Imagine the room filled with even fifty living, incarnate thieves, murderers, suicides, rapists," she said. "Would you not think carefully before inviting such beings around you?"

Logic told me that only one could use our energies at a time. I was sure I could be detached and objective about the proceedings. I was, however, becoming more and more worried about François. He was an emotional person to begin with, and frequently talked himself into a state of frenzy over the most trivial upsets. If he became emotional during a Ouija session, and if Sharma was correct, I harbored the real fear that he would make himself vulnerable and open to the powers we had encountered, whatever they might be. He had told us that when he was a child he was terrified by evil ceremonies he had witnessed. He had seen an old woman sticking pins into a doll and saying incantations over it. The fear had made him tremble and vomit. I wondered how much of that story was true and how much his own desire for drama and attention. But I could not get away from the apprehension I felt that the séance could put him in jeopardy—a kind of self-induced shock. The ironic part was that while he really did not want to participate in our sessions, he couldn't bear to miss anything. He was, like so many people, torn between his fear of not knowing the truth and his fear, if there was a truth to be found, of finding it.

Michael prepared the table, as usual, while Sharma and I cleaned up the kitchen. François remained seated, looking sullen. It was past eleven o'clock. Carefully, Michael oiled the table and touched up the letters and numbers that had faded. I lit a fresh candle and the light was switched off. We sat silently for a moment in a room dark except for the pure light of the flame.

The glass began to move as soon as we touched it, suddenly, without question or invocation, as if someone had been impatiently waiting for us to make the contact. But the glass spelled no message, and did not move smoothly around the table. The energy flow was somehow different from the way I had remembered it the weekend before. We called for Zena, but there was no response, just the jolting, halting movement of the glass.

"What's going on?" said Michael, disturbed. I looked at him: I knew that if something was amiss, Sharma would not fail to spot it. We took our fingers away from the glass and Michael ran his palm across the table surface to be sure he had oiled it correctly, but it was not the glass or the table; something else was wrong.

"It seems so different tonight," I said in an undertone, feeling alarming conflict between something like fear and the intellectual need to go on. I willed myself to be calm, detached and strong. I looked at Michael and François, and at Sharma, who sat silently, looking back at me. Then I reached out to touch the glass; they followed suit. Again the glass began to move in its erratic, disquieting way.

"What is your name, spirit?" I asked aloud. Howard wrote the letters as we relayed them and then divided them into words as before. But it was more difficult tonight. The glass touched letters twice or three times in a row uncontrolled, frenetic. On the paper Howard had written:

YYOOUURSEEARCCHISSALLOSSS

He figured out the message and read it to us:

YOUR SEARCH IS A LOSS

Michael shivered and said he felt cold. I felt a chill also. The glass struggled around the letters as Howard took everything down:

COOLDDMICHAELL (COLD MICHAEL)

"It must be the other one—Beth," said Michael, wide-eyed. "She's making it cold in here. Can't you feel it?" The glass moved again: an almost irritatingly jerking movement that made it very difficult for us to concentrate. Howard took everything down, but we had to stop while he labored to decipher it all. It just didn't make any sense:

YYYOUUUCCANNNOOTVAALIIDATTEECLAAIMMBY-YTHHHATWWAAYIWWILSSTOOPITIICOULDHHHELPP

Finally Howard looked up and read the message aloud:

YOU CANNOT VALIDATE CLAIM BY THAT WAY I WILL STOP IT I COULD HELP

"It still doesn't make any sense," he said, puzzled.

"We don't believe you," I said to the glass. The same awkward, halting procedure, before Howard read:

YOU ARE MISTAKEN

"Is your name Zena?"

NO

"Why are you here tonight?" Again the tedious message, with double letters and an almost unendurable slowness. Finally Howard read:

YOUR POWER IS NOT HER FORCE BETHLENES JUST AS STRONG

"Is your name Bethlene?"

YES

"Are you Zena's sister Beth?"

YES NO

"Who do you wish to speak to?"

ASK SHARMA

A pause while the glass moved erratically around the board, unable to touch any of the letters. Then it continued.

ZENA REGRETS

None of it made any sense to us. I was feeling a sensation of physical agitation in my stomach, and my temples were beginning to hurt. Michael was unable to concentrate fully, and seemed listless and upset. François's eyes were wide.

"Ask Sharma what?" I said with an irritation in my voice audible even to me. I sensed Sharma's concerned glance, but did not acknowledge it. I kept my eyes on the glass while Howard deciphered the hodgepodge of letters.

BETH JUST AS POWERFUL ZENA CAN BE JUST AS LONELY ASK SHARMA ABOUT LEAF GREEN FIG IS BETTER FORCE

"What the hell does this mean?" asked Michael. I motioned to him with my free hand.

"Is it Zena?"

BETH NOT ZENA

"Are you Sharma's sister?" The spirit was not making any sense.

NOT HATH EVER FOUND

"Sharma has never been found?" I asked.

NO

"Who was never found?"

ISLAND

"Island," I repeated. Perhaps, I suggested, she was trying to say something about logs or ship records having never been found. Or about Water Island, where she and Higgins lived.

"Or," said Michael in a quiet voice, "perhaps that their bodies were never found." I shuddered involuntarily. The glass began to move:

SPEAK TO ME BETHLENE BETHLENE Beth wanted our attention!

"We want to help," I said.

NO HELP NECESSARY I WILL BE HERE EVER

"Tell us your name, spirit." Testing for inconsistencies.

BETHLENE

"Your name is Bethlene?"

YES

"In what year did you die?"

1878 COLD

"You mean it was in the winter?"

HOT

"Did you die in the ocean?"

YES

"Did you drown?"

YES

"Are you buried near the house?"

ZENA TOGETHER

"Do you know Zena?"

YES

"Is she your sister?"

YES

"Do you have another sister?"

YES

"There are three sisters?"

YES

And the energy was gone, leaving us exhausted and drained. This had been more taxing on us all than had the sessions the previous weekend. The erratic movement of the glass, the frustration and oppressive physical sensations we had felt, the cold, the exasperation of waiting for long messages to be deciphered. They all took their toll. And then, when the messages were read, we were no more enlightened than we would have been if we had left them in their original garbled state.

"What on earth are we dealing with?" I asked. Obviously there was no answer. I now had no idea who these message senders were, or by what power they operated. I could not understand why the energy would be so halting and jumpy, if we had merely contacted a different spirit. Zena's messages of the weekend before had seemed cautious, sincere, with an element of caring for us—she seemed very human, perhaps too human. And yet, given Sharma's explanation that all the spirits of the astral plane desperately needed to live on through the body of a living being, Zena could have been just as evil as Beth or perhaps even more so. Beth was warning us to stay away from the board; Zena might have been wooing us, luring us into her power, playing on our desire to learn and to help.

A disquieting thought crossed my mind: If that was the case, François might not be the one in greatest jeopardy. He had nobody's interest at heart but his own. It might well be the willing ones among us who were the most vulnerable. Would my personal strength protect me?

"Do you think these spirits have sinister intents?" I asked Sharma. "I mean both of them—Zena and Beth?"

"Yes," said François with conviction.

"Don't forget that none of the spirits on the astral plane is likely to be very evolved," said Sharma, who had been sitting quietly near the table. "If they lived unsavory lives on earth, there is little chance that their afterlives would be much better. Sinister may seem strong, but certainly they are misguided and can be dangerous."

We wondered why the spirit had been so upset about having Sharma there. What had the spirit written? Howard turned back the yellow lined pages and found the spot:

ASK SHARMA ABOUT LEAF GREEN FIG IS BETTER FORCE

No one among us had any possible interpretation. But some of the information seemed to fit with Zena's: The part about the Island, and something, or someone, who was never found. And the year of her death: 1878, five years after Zena's —the stories of the two spirits seem to fit.

"If there *are* two spirits," Sharma said.

"You mean there could be only one?" Michael asked.

"It's possible. There is no way of knowing for sure."

"What about this?" asked Howard, who was looking back over the notes he had taken: "What does it mean, 'I will be here ever'?"

"I believe it means that Beth, or whoever that spirit was, is trapped in the astral plane," said Sharma. "She is clinging to the earth by her own desires and fear, not wishing to progress any further. Maybe she wishes to be there forever, holding on to the illusion of being near the living."

"But does this really go on forever?" I asked.

How could there be eternal punishment for a human life? Yet if what Sharma said was true, these spirits actually could be in a kind of hell, in which they had been waiting, clinging to the earth but not of the earth, for nearly a hundred years. How much longer would it go on for them? Why had they not been born again—if there was such a thing as reincarnation? All we had were questions, more and more of them. And not a single answer.

I stood up and turned on the chandelier, trying to stop the flow and swirl of thoughts in my pounding temples. It was nearly one thirty in the morning, and the room was still chilly, though the night was warm.

FOURTH ENCOUNTER

Saturday, July 8

"Let me ask you something," I said to Sharma the next morning on the beach. "Do you think François is safe during our séances?" I was feeling guilty, I suppose, for forcing the séance last night despite my promise to him. And now that I no longer suspected Michael of manipulating the glass in some way, I had begun to feel very uneasy about the kind of power we might be dealing with. Sharma's cautions had shaken my own self-assurance somewhat, and the previous night's session, with its terribly fatiguing energy drain, had made me question whether the strain and his fear were more than François could handle. I also knew that he had been angry at the beginning of our session. I asked Sharma, since she thought it was dangerous to take part in such proceedings in a normal mental state, if to do so while under mental stress would be an invitation to disaster.

Sharma couldn't say. She knew François was given to dramatics, and thought he might possibly put himself into a trancelike state, but whether he was especially vulnerable to attack from spirits she was unwilling to guess. She did say, however, that even a self-induced trance would be highly dangerous.

"Trance isn't really the right word," she told me. "He would probably put himself in a state of something close to shock; he would lose all conscious control. It would be as if the enormity of the situation overpowered him so that he could no longer deal with it, and he would simply cease trying. This kind of thing happens all the time to people in disasters. It would be very much the same here: François would simply be frozen with fright." She said the danger was that at these times, should a spirit have the desire and the energy, it might be able to seize upon his vulnerability and possess him. And she said it did not necessarily have to be the particular spirit we were communicating with, but any of the host that were undoubtedly in the room with us, fighting for a chance to make contact. She repeated that it was terribly dangerous for us to have the Ouija exposed when we were not actually using it—that it had turned our house into a hotbed for the spirit world now, and that it was doubly important to cover it.

"However, Arnold," she said with concern in her voice that touched me, "I would not be as concerned about François as for yourself." This took me by surprise. Surely she wasn't going to suggest that I couldn't fend off any attack from this vague otherworld. "You are very much involved with this game," she told me. "You think you are detached, that your approach is purely intellectual. You say you worry about François's vulnerability on account of his fear and self-indulgence. But you don't realize that you are yourself already beginning to be obsessed with continuing."

I wanted to contradict her, but she went on: "Arnold, please listen. You told François you would not continue; yet when you were there in the room with the board, you couldn't wait to get started. Nothing else mattered to you. And this is the danger: Your willingness and eagerness to play is an open invitation. If you contact a spirit strong enough, you'll be in just as great a danger as François, perhaps even greater."

I turned and stared out at the ocean. It was her right to say what she felt, and I appreciated her concern for me, but I was somewhat offended that she considered me prey for these spirits. Not only was I in control of myself, but for some reason I had become a kind of leader of the group, responsible for the direction of the proceedings. It was I who had asked the questions, and who was on guard, looking for clues to possible trickery. It was also I who remained detached and watchful and, unlike Michael, uninvolved, purely intellectual about it. Sharma was overreacting, probably guided by her own overcautiousness, the same cautiousness that kept her from participating with us.

"Look, I'm not even sure we've contacted spirits," I said peevishly. "So let's just drop the subject." I looked at the water, cool and inviting. I thought of going for a swim—anything to get away from the talk of spirits.

"I'm sorry if I hurt you," she said quickly, touching my arm. "But I'm just terribly concerned. Not only during the séances, but all the time. Now that you have opened yourself to these beings, it will be difficult to get rid of their influence."

"What?" I said. "What do you mean? Will I be haunted wherever I go? Nonsense."

"There's no way to tell. But it is possible."

"But can these spirits be omnipresent?" I couldn't believe it. We had conducted these séances on the coast of Long Island, and we had contacted Long Island spirits—people who had died in the coastal waters—not spirits from California or Asia. They died here and they were stuck here.

"No, not exactly omnipresent," she said, "but they can follow you somehow—attach themselves and continue with you wherever you go. I have heard of such cases, where the spirit lives with a human, waiting for the person to give in to the demand of the emotional body. Always waiting for a chance to strike."

"The emotional body?" I was getting interested again in spite of myself. I asked her to explain.

She took a breath, hesitating, gathering her thoughts.

"The great teachers say that each of us is made of several bodies—physical, emotional, and mental. The physical body, of course, is what we can see and touch. It needs nourishment, and performs all the physical functions. This body is very important, but it is not *you*."

"What do you mean? Of course it's me. "

"No," she said. "The real *you* is your spirit, your soul, your essence. It never dies; it is immortal and only changes bodies and environments for experience and evolvement. It lives within your other bodies." Sharma sensed my impatience. "Just think," she said, "when the demands of the physical body get out of hand, what happens? It becomes fat, or addicted to smoking, drugs, medicine, and even food. This is because the essential you has not been able to take charge, to stop the compulsions to which we are all prone."

"I understand that, but what about the other bodies?"

"Besides the physical body, we also have an emotional body. If you indulge in great displays of emotion, whether they be feelings of lust or anger, *you* are not in control; your emotional body is."

"What about love," I challenged. "Is love not an emotion?"

"It depends upon what you mean by love. Love is not an emotional sensation churned by ecstasy and sensuality. These are extremes which can cause jealousy and possessiveness. People who turn themselves inside out for this kind of love, living only to please their lovers or themselves, usually become very unhappy, resentful people in the end. I do not happen to believe this is love in its true sense. Love to me is something on a much higher level."

"And the mental body?" Could this be the "self" her rather complex theory kept referring to?

"Not at all," she said. "The mental body is like a machine, a computer, that runs the physical and sifts the data presented by the world through a screen called logic. The mental body tries to confuse you with thoughts, information, runnings and rerunnings of past conversations or possible future ones. It daydreams and wanders. The mental body is extremely important, but it can be insidious, too. People—especially intellectuals—tend to rely on their minds to tell them the truth, to figure out their lives for them according to learned, logical criteria."

I began to react negatively to this. I had a rather intellectual approach to life, and it had always served me well. What was insidious about it?

"But don't you see that to act on the basis of reason alone is limiting? It clouds the greater truths."

I bristled.

"Thinking itself can be very creative," Sharma went on, placatingly. "Thoughts can give life to ideas. But it also can be destructive. Think of the brilliance of famous criminals, madmen, and leaders of nations who manipulate others solely for power. They are driven by their mental bodies. But truth—truth is intuitive. That is why it's so important to keep your consciousness high, your thoughts and actions free from personal achievement at the cost of others."

"You make it sound as if people are nothing but corks on some cosmic sea," I told her. "Surely we have more control of our destinies than that."

"A good metaphor," she said. "Many people are like corks on the sea, going through their own private evolutions. We live our own lifetimes, and develop our own karmas. Before we can even begin to glimpse our true selves, we must know what it is to live by the dictates of the physical, emotional, and mental bodies." She stopped for a moment, considering. I began to speak, but she continued suddenly:

"And that is also why you're putting yourself in unnecessary danger, pursuing this game which we can't possibly understand." She shrugged. "But if you continue, I suppose it's just your karma; and whatever happens, that will be your karma, too. You'll have to work it out."

Sharma said she thought Michael was already on the verge of being possessed. She said that she wouldn't be surprised if he were to become involved in some kind of cult should the opportunity present itself. Sharma liked Michael and was genuinely concerned for him. I myself thought Sharma was getting a little carried away. Theories about reincarnation and the evolution of the soul were interesting enough to listen to, but she actually subscribed to all this. It was a bit much. As for her concern for Michael, I found it laughable that she thought an intelligent person in the twentieth century would get himself involved in any kind of devil cult. I associated cults with the Dark Ages, with secret proceedings in darkened caverns. My imagination ran to the Gothic, to the Hellfire Club, to the Salem Trials.

But Sharma told me there actually existed a coven of witches on the North Shore of Long Island, not fifty miles from where we sat in the broad summer sun. Such things do, indeed, go on, she assured me, stung by my reaction. There always are some who are attracted to the dark side of life. And they find one another.

I remembered something she had said—about Eastern teachers being able to cut through the astral plane to higher regions. What made her so sure we couldn't do the same?

"Impossible!" she said. "I have not the slightest doubt that they're coming straight from the astral plane. Don't you see the emotional struggle that takes place at the table when you play? Don't you feel your emotions more than any other part of you? Can you truly say that it's your intellect that's in control when you engage the Ouija?" She explained that the emotional body and the astral body are two names for the same thing. That the astral plane is so called because it is the place where all the souls go who are under the control of their emotional bodies. Our very desire to try to make a Ouija in the first place was astral in nature, she said. It was our emotional nature that impelled us, not our intellect.

I was becoming more and more perplexed by this conversation. On the one hand, I didn't want to accept any of it. But on the other, I found parts of what Sharma said ringing disturbingly true.

I shuddered involuntarily in the warm sun. I tried to accept all she had said as a matter of curiosity, reminding myself that the Eastern mind tended naturally to be passive, while the Western mind was more active and inquisitive. I looked at the sky—the sun was high. We had been so engrossed in conversation that we had not noticed the time passing. I suddenly realized I was hungry, and rounded up the others for lunch.

Later in the afternoon Sharma and I walked up the beach to Water Island, which was not really an island at all, but a small community to the east of us on Fire Island. We had friends there—Hank, a film producer, and his wife, Melissa, a screenwriter. It was an easy twenty-five-minute walk. We walked slowly along the edge of the sea, Sharma's dog, Tiger, splashing in the surf, enjoying himself.

Water Island was an isolated place. No roads or boardwalks led to it, so it was impossible to get there from the main ferry unless you wanted to walk along the beach or take a sand taxi. People who had their houses there had to carry all their belongings by water in small launches. The bay in the area was very shallow, so some of the people actually had to use two boats—a motor launch from the dock, and then shallow-draft dinghies moored beyond the shoals, in which they would row their goods from launch to house in as many trips as were necessary. Because of the inconveniences involved in getting anything over there, most of the people of Water Island lived extremely simply.

But it was a beautiful area, thickly wooded with many pines, some birches, and a few oaks and holly trees. The government had protected it as a natural preserve—a National Seashore—which made the area an inviting one for all kinds of birds. Egrets, cardinals, every kind of woodpecker, and hummingbirds. The unspoiled look of Water Island was enhanced by the fact that no electricity had yet been brought in. People cooked with bottled gas and read either in the sunshine or by the light of oil lamps at night.

Hank and Melissa's summer cottage faced the sea. The shingles had been weathered silver by strong winds, and the roof sloped protectively down to a broad covered deck which could more properly be called a porch. It was nearly three thirty by the time Sharma and I arrived.

Melissa was sitting on the beach in front of the house. She was a beautiful woman, tall, big-boned, with long brown hair and blue eyes surrounded by thick, dark lashes.

"It's almost teatime," she said, glad to see us.

"But we do it American style—iced, and on the beach." We followed Melissa into the house, and Hank came in from the back room, where he had been working on a script.

While Melissa made tea, the conversation naturally turned to our new summer house, how we liked it, and how we had been spending our time. The most exciting thing, of course, was a *verboten* subject, which I knew I shouldn't mention. But I couldn't resist, knowing how Melissa loved the unusual and bizarre. As I spoke I knew I was wrong to do so.

Melissa was immediately interested. Hank, the jokester, made some remark to the effect that we were all "raising the devil," but Melissa shushed him. "No," she said, "it's very serious. When can we come and watch?"

Now this was something I had not considered —that anyone outside our group would be interested in joining in. I had no personal objections, but I told them I thought it should be cleared with the others. The truth was that we had not yet made plans to have another séance even tonight. How could I commit myself to continuing something I was not at all sure ought to be continued?

Melissa was extremely interested and wanted to know all the details. Sharma was called upon more than once to explain certain phenomena. And then, Melissa had a story of her own to tell us:

She had been a guest a few years back in an old house in Connecticut owned by the family of some friends of hers. One night, when everyone had gone to bed, Melissa had retired to her own room to sleep. At about three in the morning she was awakened by a strange sensation—not a sound, but something in the room that brought her out of sleep. She opened her eyes and saw at the foot of her bed a young soldier dressed in a uniform of the Union Army. He beckoned to her with his hand to come and follow him. Melissa was not in the least frightened, but very curious about why this man had suddenly appeared in costume in her bedroom. She spoke to him, but he did not reply. He only beckoned her, turned and walked a few steps toward the door, and beckoned her again to follow.

Melissa got up and threw a dressing gown around her shoulders. She followed the soldier out into the hall, down the stairs, and out the front door. It was summer, and the night was clear and warm, but Melissa felt the dampness of the dew as she walked in her bare feet across the grass. Even in the warmth of the air, she said, the dampness made her feel chilly. She had to walk very fast to keep up with the soldier. She called out for him to slow down, and asked him where they were going, but he only stopped, beckoned again, and went on into the darkness. The soldier led Melissa into a broad meadow, always going faster and faster—until suddenly he vanished. He did not disappear into the distance, she said. She had her eyes on him, and suddenly he was not there anymore. She stopped, stood there searching the landscape to no avail, and decided to go back to the house. She was met at the door by her hostess, who had awakened during the night and noticed Melissa's bedroom light on. When she told her hostess the story, the woman was visibly affected. She took Melissa to the library and showed her a large family journal the original owners of the house had kept. In it was a record of a son who had joined the Union Army at the age of eighteen. He was wounded during battle, but refused against orders to be kept in the field hospital. He made his escape one night and found his way home. His body had been discovered not far from the house in the field nearby. The journal showed entries after his death, made by another member of the family who had seen him walking in his uniform through the fields. Melissa had been too shaken by the story to go back to sleep, so she stayed up reading for a while, and finally drifted off with the light still on. In the morning, she at first could not decide if it had all been a dream or had really happened. She went down to the library —the journal was still out, opened to the page she had read during the night. Her hostess asked her later to fill in her account of what had occurred the night before.

I was captivated by the firsthand experience, and there was no doubt in my mind that if our séances were to continue, Melissa had to be a part of them. I invited them to come to the house for dinner on the following Saturday with the reservation that I would call them in town to confirm the invitation during the week after clearing it with the others. I could sense Sharma's disapproval, but she said nothing.

The table was set that night with a tablecloth. I made a supreme effort to control myself and did not mention Melissa and Hank, except to say that we had seen them. I did not tell the story of Melissa's remarkable experience, even to Michael. We had agreed, after all, not to talk with anyone about what we were doing. And I was afraid that, if the others knew I had revealed our secret, they would want to stop. I decided to tell them later that Hank and Melissa were coming for dinner the following Saturday, and when Saturday came I would just let them stay. François made us promise that we would not attempt to contact any spirits that evening. And promise we did in a roundabout way. I knew it was devious and wrong, and that, according to Sharma's reasoning at least, I should be keeping my consciousness high and my motives pure. I told myself that I had discussed our séances with outsiders because of my curiosity and desire to learn about the phenomenon. Now that I knew others were familiar with such things, I was no longer as afraid of being thought crazy. But I knew that when I had told Melissa my only motivation was to tell my sensational story to one who loved the unusual. I just couldn't help it. Whether any of the others had been talking about it outside of the group I had no idea.

There was no question that we would hold a séance that evening, especially for Michael and me, despite our promise to François. If the others had misgivings about it, they were welcome to go out. I noticed that Howard, for all his skepticism, was still with us. François had yet to leave the house rather than participate. We had had only three sessions, though it seemed the Ouija had already become an established part of the weekends.

Again, Sharma was present at the table but did not participate. She sat quietly at my side, watching—and watchful. When the room was still, and the only light was the candle in its heavy glass ashtray, Michael, François, and I reached purposefully, ritualistically, and touched the glass. Immediately there was a smooth surge of energy. Tiger, who had been peacefully resting on his mistress' lap, became suddenly alert and whined briefly.

Without our asking any questions, the glass moved smoothly from letter to letter. I spoke the letters aloud for Howard to record. Michael said it must be Zena—he could recognize her energy, as could I. It was as recognizable as a familiar voice. The spirit wrote:

SHE IS VERY UNEASY

"Is that you, Zena?" I asked.

ZENA BETH IS GONE I RETURN ZENA

The energy stopped. But we were sure it would begin again as it had in the past when Zena had left and said that she would return. We waited quietly and patiently once more. Our fingers never left the glass. In a few minutes I felt the return of the energy, and the glass began its smooth, rapid motion once more:

MAY NOT RETURN NOW CAN YOU TEST ME TO-MORROW

"Is that you, Zena?" I asked.

MISTRUST YOU TEST ME   A pause.   OTHERS MORE TRUSTING

"Who mistrusts?"

ALL OF YOU YOU HAVE DISTRUST BETH NEVER INTENDED THAT SHE BE INVOLVED I MUST HUNT FOR HER

"Hunt for Beth?" I asked. François grew nervous and said he didn't want Beth here.

YES

"Are you calling her here?" I asked.

"No!" François shouted, half rising from his chair. "Not Beth." Sharma put a hand on François's arm, and he quieted.

NO MORE NOW MUST RETURN

"You are Zena?"

YES

"Will you be back again?"

YES MY PATIENT FRIENDS

"Can we tell anybody about you?"

TRUST THOSE NO MORE NOW TRUST ARNOLD FRANCOIS HOWARD MICHAEL I AM UPSET WITH BETHLENE GOOD NIGHT   And the energy ceased.

As soon as I felt the abrupt cessation of the energy flow, François jerked back from the table as if he had been released from a magnetic grasp. He was ashen-faced, and unable to speak. Sharma quickly snapped on the light and Howard went to get him a glass of water. In a few minutes he seemed able to regain his composure, but his eyes reflected the resentment and anger he harbored inside for all of us, and, I suspected, for me most of all. He got up and went into his bedroom without uttering a single word. Dramatics, I told myself.

The rest of us sat around the table for a few minutes more. Michael quietly covered the Ouija board with a white cloth and sat down again. We were full of questions. We were worried about François, but this session had once again been so unlike the others we had experienced that we had to stay and discuss it. Howard flipped back through his notes.

Zena had told us to trust no others. Had she meant living or dead? Sharma could be right, there might be other spirits. On the other hand, Zena seemed annoyed that we had tested to see if she really was Zena. Michael suggested that she might have been preoccupied with Beth.

But during the other sessions she had instructed us to test to see if we were indeed contacting her. I was beginning to get a crawly sensation at the back of my neck. It seemed that Zena was trying to assure herself of our exclusive attention. She did not want us making contact with other spirits —but she wanted to be sure the Ouija would remain open for her. "Can you test me tomorrow?" she had asked. But we wouldn't be there tomorrow night. Was Zena trying to keep us there all the time? Did she await us during the week, longing for another chance to contact the physical universe, agonizing over the time?

"Trust those no more," the spirit had said when I asked if we could tell anyone about her. She might have been objecting to my conversation with Sharma, or even with Melissa and Hank. Sharma, who knew something about the spirit world, might present an obstacle to the completion of Zena's objectives, whatever they might be. Why would she instruct us not to trust anyone but her?

And what about the animals' reactions? Tiger seemed to sense the presence of the spirits. Sharma told us that animals are very psychic. She said the belief in the East was that dogs and cats were put on earth for the sole purpose of experiencing the love of human beings; it was a part of their souls' evolution. That is why, she said, the best training for dogs is based on love—dogs feel only love for their masters and want only to obey. If they are treated cruelly, they feel intensely lonely or resentful. She told us dogs and cats could sense things that humans cannot. And when they sense danger, from this dimension or some other one, they growl or shy away from it as instinctively as if someone were reaching for a strap to beat them.

"But people are psychic, too," she said. "Not just a few—many, many people. It is a part of our natural evolution, although not many people recognize it."

FIFTH ENCOUNTER

Friday, July 14

The Monday following that weekend was one of those rare New York days when the sky was the color of periwinkle and uninterrupted by clouds. The city was a welcome relief from the rigors of the weekend.

At about one o'clock I picked up my car and headed up the FDR Drive toward a little upholstery shop on East 103rd Street where I was having some furniture made. The northbound lanes were heavy with cars traveling densely at about forty miles an hour. I kept to the slow lane nearest the concrete wall that divided the highway from the East River.

Suddenly my car seemed to wrench itself out of my control.

"My God, what's going on!" I said aloud. I grasped the wheel and tried to straighten it, but there was a strong and relentless pull working against me. I slammed on the brakes; they did not respond. The car jerked to the right, jumped a small meridian, and straddled it for some twenty feet. I could hear the car's undersides ripping out in a continuous, wrenching disembowelment. I gripped the wheel and pulled it to the left with all my strength, but still something counteracted me with incredible force. The car spun again to the right and crashed headlong into the concrete bulkhead. There was a thunderous crunch of pleating metal.

The traffic continued to rush past me. Through a honeycomb of glass I saw the concrete wall—only a few feet of crumpled beige metal between it and me. I pulled on the door latch. It stuck. I pulled again, harder, and threw my weight against the door. It groaned open and I got out. I felt dizzy. I held onto the door to steady myself, and stood there, unable to account for what had happened.

Before I knew it the police arrived. The first thing they said when they saw my car was, "You should be dead." I was totally confused. How did it happen? I asked myself. "Are you O.K.?" one of them asked. I assured them that I was, but my car, I thought, my beautiful new car. It was completely ruined.

I told the police that I had swerved to avoid hitting a car that had cut in front of me from the next lane. The police sent for a tow truck and offered to drive me to the hospital, but I refused. I only wanted to continue with the schedule I had already planned. They looked at me dubiously, trying to decide whether I was really O.K. When I insisted that I was perfectly fine and late for my appointment, they drove me over to First Avenue, where I found a taxi. I went on to 103rd Street and kept my appointment, took a subway home, and immediately called my insurance broker.

I sat down on the sofa and stared straight ahead of me, seeing nothing in the room, trying to think back to the exact moment of the accident. Why had I lost control of the car? I remembered the bafflement I had felt along with the alarm, and an involuntary shudder rippled up my back. I tried to concentrate on the exact thoughts I had had, but I could not keep my mind on the subject. Something in me did not want to examine it. And now my head was beginning to ache. The accident replayed itself again and again, until nothing made sense anymore.

When I awoke on Tuesday morning, my head was much improved. I felt a slight tingling sensation, but nothing else was wrong. The first thing I did was telephone my family. They were all aghast that I had not called before, and that the police had not insisted on taking me to the hospital. I gave them all the physical details, and ended the conversation as quickly as possible.

Howard and François had to be called so they would have time to arrange for other transportation to the house that weekend. But when I called Michael, I knew I had to see him in person. I had serious misgivings about the accident and I had to discuss it with him. We arranged to meet for lunch on Thursday. What hung over me like an ominous cloud was the unjustifiable idea that an invisible power outside of myself had been able to wrench away from me the controls of my own car. A ridiculous hypothesis, I knew, trying to shove it out of my mind. I was overdramatizing, it was paranoid, it was insane. I didn't want to consider it. But Sharma's warning that spirits can travel with you hounded me. Choosing my words carefully, I told Michael, stacking the deck so he would laugh the idea out of my mind. I wanted him to tell me I was crazy, that of course it had been me and nobody else who had willfully steered my own car into a concrete wall. But he did not. He told me that to drive into a wall at forty miles an hour was against all the laws of self-preservation. I stared at him across the lunch table, my mind not willing to accept it. No one mentioned the word spirit—but Michael said the only way to be sure of what it was that we were dealing with was to continue and try to uncover more information. I agreed: We needed to know more. In fact, I suggested we accelerate the pace of the séances. We were going too slowly, I told Michael. We were taking too much time thinking about what we were doing, and not enough time getting information. We had no idea how much longer we could continue. Perhaps Saturday's séance had been our last. I irrationally blamed François for delaying our progress.

"I don't want to dither around with this all

summer," I said irritably, thinking of François but knowing part of my irritation was directed inward, at myself. "Why don't you and I do the Ouija by ourselves? Without François there, we might get some questions answered. Do you think the two of us alone can get the energy level high enough?"

Michael stopped eating. "I have been developing a theory," he said. "I think that you and I are, in fact, the only ones at the table who have anything to do with the spirits' ability to contact us. I can feel a certain flow, not only through my fingers on the glass, but into my body from somewhere else. It's not something I can focus on or concentrate on. I let my mind simply open and not really think of anything, and it happens."

I had felt the same sort of incoming energy flow and I knew what he was talking about. And yet Michael always seemed to be much more involved than I. "Are you aware of what's going on around you?" I asked.

"Oh yes, quite sharply, in fact," he said. "I find my consciousness is heightened. I am aware not only of the influx of energy, but of everything that goes on in the room—the sound of the ocean, every word spoken, every letter touched by the glass. Sometimes I can keep up with the glass mentally so well that I know even long messages before Howard reads them. It's difficult to explain."

Michael felt that he was the receiver of the energy from the spirit world, and that somehow my own energy amplified the impulses. The glass was the point on which we were both focusing our energies. Michael called the joining of energy "kinetic energy," which literally means "the energy of action."

I found his theory curious and interesting, especially the sensations he felt during the séances. The energy I felt was quite different, and I did not feel that I was opening myself in the way Michael described. I was concentrating so intensely that I was aware of very little other than the Ouija, and sometimes of the reactions of the people around the table. I wondered if Michael, in the process of receiving the energy, was putting himself in any danger. I wondered if opening himself, allowing himself to become so close to the energy sources, was a necessary part of the process, or if he was needlessly making himself vulnerable. Michael did not think he was in danger, but neither did he seem to mind the idea much. I had felt on more than one occasion that Michael would almost have welcomed, in a morbid sort of way, the experience of being possessed. Michael was the kind who would try literally anything, including unusual sex experiments, at least once.

Michael laughed off my concern and told me to think of myself. My God, maybe he's right, I thought. Who was I fooling? It was I who had just nearly been killed.

Michael and I agreed that the two of us ought to try to conduct a séance by ourselves this coming weekend, to see if his theory was correct. Also, if the beings we were contacting were psychic products of our own minds rather than spiritual visitations (the only two possibilities remaining, now that I no longer suspected Michael of trickery), this would eliminate two possible sources of energy, Howard and François. We decided to try tactfully to get rid of both of them.

That evening I had dinner at Sharma's house. I had not told her about the car accident. I had not wanted to have my irrational fears corroborated until I had had a chance to think them through and discuss them with Michael at lunch. I walked over to her house; she lived nearby in the West Village. Sharma was in the kitchen; I stood in the doorway, leaning against the frame, chatting with her as she cooked. I wasn't sure I should tell her about the accident, but I couldn't hold back. I needed to tell her.

She stopped stirring and looked up at me. Her dark eyes were filled with the most touching concern. "Your fears are not unfounded," she told me, "but there is still more to the accident than this. It was not merely that an entity seized control of your car, but that it willfully and maliciously tried to destroy you." She was very worried, and she pleaded with me not to do the Ouija anymore, to stop now, before it was too late.

"Your curiosity is not healthy, it's morbid. You will get no information that will help you, and you can see now how much actual harm can come to you."

I wondered if she was right, and knew she had given me good advice before. I took her in my arms, comforting myself as much as Sharma. "I'll consider what you say," I told her, and kissed her to show her I meant it.

That night I did not stay at Sharma's apartment. I had to be alone. I could sense that she was still upset about my accident and I knew she doubted that I would be able to give up my dealings with Zena and Beth. I felt deeply sorry for being the cause of her heartache, but it made me feel better to know that she understood I would continue. Because I could not give it up, not yet. Everything she said—anything anyone said—seemed to stoke the flame of my curiosity rather than quench it. I looked forward to the following evening more intensely than ever.

Being carless in the city was one thing—I hardly used it anyway—but getting to the country on Friday afternoon became a major nuisance. I had had no word yet from the insurance company, but I had been consoled by the investigators, who had told me that I would have no trouble collecting the full amount for the car. However, it looked as if it would be some time before I would have a car again, so I arranged to go to Fire Island by train that weekend. The others would be driving out later on with friends.

Joshua, Rachel, and I took the Long Island Rail Road to Sayville. The dogs were on a double lead and very frisky. But they were used to travel-

ing and soon settled down enough for me to take
their leashes off. The seats of the passenger car
were extremely hard; they were covered with
straw-colored lacquered wicker, and hinged at the
bottom so they could be flipped one way or the
other—enabling you to sit facing either the front
or the rear of the train. Since it wasn't crowded,
I adjusted two neighboring seats to form a pair
of facing booths, one for me, one for the dogs. I
put my suitcase down on the floor to keep them
in—a psychological pacifier for the conductor,
since I knew the puppies would not attempt to
escape. I propped my feet, ankles crossed, on the
opposite banquette, and the puppies arranged
themselves in an overlapping pile. I settled down
to read my book on reincarnation. I was wearing
a straw hat that day, which I had to tilt forward
on my head as I slouched against the incredibly
rigid seatback.

From Sayville I had to take a taxi to the dock,
where I threw my suitcase onto the pier with
some other people's baggage and went to a nearby
diner to wait for the next ferry. Cars were beginning to arrive, and the few people on the pier
were stashing their baggage and groceries on the
dock, to be loaded by the boatmen. I could see
the ferry churning its way homeward, but she
was still fairly far offshore and I had time for
an iced tea before she docked.

An hour later we came to a rumbling stop on
the far shore. I loaded the dogs and suitcase into
our hand wagon, unlocked the padlock that se-

cured it to the fence, and pulled it along the board-walk, wheels creaking, the restless puppies making it difficult to maneuver.

We arrived at the house at about four thirty; nobody else was there. I turned the dogs loose on the beach and set about opening the doors and windows to let the house air out, then changed into my trunks and a sweat shirt and went out to the beach to read. There were very few people in sight. After a quick dip, I settled down to read until I noticed that the air began to feel chilly. I looked up; the sun was very low, and I was now alone on the beach except for Joshua and Rachel. I pulled on my shirt. Off to the east, the dunes were cast with gold from the low afternoon sun, and the trees beyond them were edged with fiery light. Birds were circling high overhead, moody, like the moody sea. I noticed how changeable the sea was, how it turned colors with the light, and reflected on the way it altered its character with the face and force of the moon. Now it was the color of tourmaline in the setting sun; at night it would be black and shining, like a raw slice of obsidian, and just as lethal. A couple of figures came into view far down the beach, people in rolled-up jeans and sweat shirts, strolling soundlessly along the edges of the sea. I stood up shivering in the breeze, and took the wet dogs to the deck to dry off before going inside to shower and change.

François and Michael were just arriving as I

came out of the bedroom. They had driven out separately but had been on the same ferry. Michael immediately got into his trunks and went swimming. François took a bag of groceries to the kitchen and began preparations for dinner. I put on some music and stood around the kitchen chatting with François while he worked. My plan was to find some way to maneuver him out of the house that evening.

I had told François about the car accident, but he did not know what I suspected had really happened. I carefully stayed off the subject, and he was more interested in the amount of insurance money I would be collecting, anyway. He also had news: He was very excited about a photograph he had had published in *Vogue*—and he was delighting in showing it to me. It was a good fashion shot. François was certainly a competent photographer. I took a knife and began slicing tomatoes for him.

"Have any plans for the evening?" I asked.

"I think we should all go out tonight for a change," François said.

"Why don't we wait and see what the others feel like doing?" I suggested. We fenced around, neither willing to commit ourselves to a trap we would be bound to later. But for François it was a double bind: He didn't want to stay, and he didn't want to be left out.

Michael strode back through the house, his shiny black hair dripping wet, and announced that he was going to take a nap. "Call me when dinner's ready," he said, and disappeared into his room.

Howard arrived, exhausted, slammed down his briefcase and his overnight bag, and headed straight for the gin. His train had been late, and he was harried and overworked. He took a shower, then made a drink, with which he collapsed onto a living-room daybed. He and I sat and talked for a while, relaxing, waiting for dinner.

At no time did any of our conversations even hint about the plans Michael and I had made for the evening's session. Howard couldn't have cared less, and was full of news and topics he found much more interesting. Michael, who staggered blearily out of the bedroom when François called, did not have to say a word. As far as he was concerned, the plans had been made. I bided my time.

It was only after we began eating that Howard mentioned, laughing, that we had forgotten the tablecloth. Michael and I flashed each other a look, but continued eating. François caught the look.

"Oh, no," he said, "you're not going to do this again. Not tonight. Two weekends was enough. Let's go out someplace."

"François, we just have to go on," I said. "But perhaps you could go out and visit some friends just for tonight."

"Well, maybe I will go out," François said angrily. "I certainly don't want to sit around with this foolishness anymore."

Michael, however, was about to take no chances of having our experiment spoiled. "Arnold and I have decided that we would like to have a go at the Ouija by ourselves this evening," he said gravely. "We want to see if we can get the energy to work with just the two of us present, and find out if we can exert any willful control over the spirits."

"If there are spirits," I added.

Howard gave us his you're-both-nuts look, but was delighted to be excused. In fact, he had been planning to go dancing anyway. François became quite hostile once he found out that we wanted to get rid of him, but he said, belligerently, that he was certainly going out because the fact was that the stupid game bored him to death. Satisfied, Michael and I got up and began clearing the things off the table. Now that everything was arranged, we couldn't wait to begin. The others disappeared into the bedrooms to change. Howard, whistling, was out the door within ten minutes, but when Michael and I were ready to begin, there was François in the living room, stretched out on one of the daybeds, reading.

"I thought you were going out," Michael said, controlling his irritation.

"No, I think I'll stay here and read, after all," François said. Michael frowned, but there was, of course, nothing either of us could do. It was François's house as much as ours.

"O.K., but we are going ahead as planned, just the two of us," I said firmly. "We want to do this without interruption." I admit that I was rather tough about it, but I was annoyed with him. The presence of another person in the room was encumbering, and the person was François into the bargain. Michael and I stood silently, conspicuously, watching François read, until he got the hint and took his book into his bedroom and closed the door. Michael turned out the lights, and I lit the candle. The room was dark except for the candle and a thread of light beneath François's bedroom door.

We sat down. The pad and pencil were beside me; tonight Michael would call the letters and I would write. We composed ourselves quietly for a few moments. Then we reached out simultaneously and touched the glass.

I felt the familiar pulse of energy, but the glass did not spin around the letters as it usually did. It remained still in the center of the table.

"Are there any spirits present?" I asked.

The glass moved rapidly and smoothly from letter to letter.

ZENA

We knew it was Zena. The glass moved again.

Michael said the letters strangely, in a voice that seemed to come from somewhere else. I wrote them down with my right hand, keeping my left hand on the glass. It was difficult to get used to the unusual procedure.

SHE IS NOT ALLOWED

"Who is not allowed?"

BETH

"Is it Zena who is here now?"

YES ZENA

"Can we ask you more about the shipwreck now?"

LET ME BETH IS NOT ALLOWED

The glass began to move with jumps and jerks, not touching any letter or number, almost as if there were a tug-of-war, a play for power, taking place on the board.

"Do you have something to tell us, Zena?" I asked.

YOU ASK ME

"Are you upset?"

NEVER ALLOW BETH TO BE

"Is she your true sister?"

YES

"Were there other sisters or brothers?"

NO BETH LIES YOU MUST NEVER

"How do you keep Beth away?"

I CONTROL HER

"You control Beth?"

EVIL

I shuddered momentarily, although it was not cold. I could read these brief messages as soon as I had written them. They needed no decoding.

"Did Beth drown, too?"

SHE NEVER HELPED ME

"Were others drowned, too?"

YES

"Others on board with you?"

YES

"And you came from Liverpool?"

YES

"We don't understand what year it was you were drowned. Was it in 1873 or 1878?"

1873

"Where did the ship sink?"

ALREADY TOLD

"Your grave is near our house, right?"

YES

"Was the ship an English one?"

YES WERE LIKE CATTLE MANY PEOPLE

"Was Higgins the Captain?"

YES NO

"Was there more than one Captain?"

YES NEVER ASK ME ABOUT CAPTAIN HIGGINS OR ABOUT BETH AND HIM

"Were they lovers?" I persevered.

YES

"Was he the father of Rosamond?"

NO NOT KNOWN WE HAD TO LEAVE OUR HOME ROSAMOND NOT MY CHILD BETHLENES CHILD SHE BLAMED ME   It took a long time to decipher this message. Michael waited, his concentration deep, uninterrupted.

"How did Beth escape the sinking ship?"

SHE WAS NOT WITH US WITH HIGGINS ABOVE ROSAMOND NOT MY CHILD

"Did Beth tell Higgins that Rosamond was your child and not hers?"

YES BLAMED ME ROSAMOND HERS

"How old was Beth then?"

28

"How old were you?"

35

"Where were you bound for?"

COTTON MILL

"Whereabouts in America?"

BINGHAMTON

"What happened to the ship?"

UNDER ALL OTHERS

"Are there more ships in the sea nearby?"

YES MORE NEAR

The glass suddenly began to sling back and forth across the circle of letters, never stopping at any of them. "Beth again," Michael said. We applied some pressure to the glass, and it stopped completely. But when we released it, the erratic tug-of-war resumed, and we knew that Beth was trying to gain control.

"We want to speak to Zena only!" I said loudly.

ALLOW ME TO CONTROL BETHS INFLUENCE A pause as I wrote, then more erratic movements, and a maddeningly halting struggle to get the messages written.

SHE IS CAPABLE OF HARM TO ALL

"What about the influence over Rosamond? Does she control her?"

I HAD TO SECURE HER

"You mean you have hidden Rosamond from Beth?"

THAT IS WHY I AM HERE

"Why does she want to influence us?"

HER DAMNATION ETERNAL SHE MUST INFLU-
ENCE

I deciphered the message and felt an ugly sensation growing in the pit of my stomach. I closed
my eyes for a moment, but when I opened them
to read the message to Michael I saw not only his
face, but another, suddenly looming in the flick-
ering candlelight. I gasped and instinctively
pushed away from the table, my heart pounding.
Michael started, alarmed.

François! He had stolen silently in to the living
room without our noticing him. Neither of us
knew how long he had been standing there. I
could have strangled him, but I suppressed my
anger. I closed my eyes and, adrenalin still pump-
ing, took several deep breaths, forcing myself to
remain calm. We pulled our chairs back to the
table, touched the glass, and began again. I read
the message out loud:

HER DAMNATION ETERNAL SHE MUST INFLU-
ENCE

"And if she is allowed to influence others?" I
asked.

IF I ALLOW HER TO BECOME STRONG THEN
WHAT HAPPENED TO YOU LAST SUMMER ARNOLD
WILL HAPPEN TO OTHERS

I thought for a moment, but could remember
nothing. Then it hit me: I had nearly drowned
the summer before, and it was to this very house
that I had been brought.

The glass began to move again.

I CAN HEAR ALL YOUR THOUGHTS SHE CAN ALSO
"You mean Beth can also hear?"

SHE IS DAMNED TO LONELINESS THAT IS WHY
SHE WANTS OUT HERE NO HARM WILL COME TO
ANY OF YOU AS LONG AS I HELP I KNOW OF YOUR
PRESENCE

"Zena, tell us how you feel," I said. "Are you
restless?"

NOW I CAN HAVE A REPRIEVE IN MY LONELI-
NESS A LONG TIME ALONE DO NOT FEAR I MEAN
GOOD

"How can we help you?"

I SPEAK THAT IS ENOUGH NO ONE HAS EVER
HEARD THIS STORY ALL SURVIVORS THOUGHT BETH
A GREAT HELP

"Is Beth a danger to us?"

I CAN WATCH OUT FOR BETH WAIT I AM JUST A
SISTER BUT I CANNOT ALLOW HER There was
another struggle for the glass; it was out of our
control. The energy changed character immediately, and the glass staggered haltingly from letter to letter. François shivered.

I AM JUST AS STRONG

"It must be Beth," Michael whispered.

SHE IS NOT HERE WAIT SHE IS STILL HERE A
pause. BETH SHE IS STRONG I CANNOT ALLOW
BETH TO STAY The glass paused again. NO SHE
IS GONE ZENA

"What's happening?" I asked. "Is that you,
Zena?"

YES

"How do we know if it is not Beth lying to us?"

SHE CAN BE NOTICED BY THE COLD GONE NOW
DO NOT FEAR SHE WILL NOT HARM MICHAEL AR-
NOLD VERY STRONG

"Do you have more to tell us?"

I KNOW THAT TIME IS LATE BUT MUCH TO TELL
ONCE TONIGHT OVER BETH WILL NOT BOTHER US

The energy stopped. Michael and I had proved that we could indeed operate the Ouija ourselves, and we had a great deal of information to work with.

It was very late, but we went back over everything that had been written. The conversation was more difficult to reconstruct tonight. Howard had usually recorded questions and answers; I had taken down only the spirits' replies. When we came to the message about what had happened to me the previous summer, Michael stopped.

"What did it mean?" he asked quietly. "What did happen?"

I clearly remembered the terrifying sensation of not simply sinking, but of being dragged under by what I had thought was the relentless current. My God, I thought, could that really have been Beth? Could she somehow have known who I was and anticipated my interference in her world?

"And what about your accident?"

It was François's voice, thin and hesitant, out of the darkness. Michael and I both turned and stared at him: How could he have guessed?

Saturday, July 15

I was awakened by the sunrise. Howard was still deep in sleep. Silently, I drew on a pair of swimming trunks and a sweat shirt and stole out of the room. I made myself some coffee and took the puppies outside to the deck, where they bounded off onto the beach while I sat on the cool, smooth boards and looked out to the sea. The colors of dawn were spread in a watery wash acrss sea and sky—all tones of gray: pink-gray, blue-gray, lavender-gray. The sun was up, but still low and unseen behind a mountain of purple-gray clouds that sloped up to the northeast. I was alone on the beach, and it was good to be alone. I needed time to myself, away from the others' fears and excitement and warnings and opinions. I needed time to ponder all that had gone before. The accident was still uppermost in my mind. Even though I had sensed some force outside myself was in command of the car, it was not until last night, when I was feeling the energy through my own body, that I began to realize the enormity of unseen powers.

I walked down the wooden steps and across the beach, feeling the cool texture of the sand under my bare feet. I stood in the surf for a few moments, sipping the hot coffee, thinking:

"What happened to you may happen to others."

Did it really mean my near-drowning? Was everything a vast coincidence, and were our imaginations playing on the facts? In our eagerness to believe in psychic phenomena, were we creating one, then blaming it for ordinary events in our everyday existence? This idea was just as staggering. But what if spirits really existed? If they tried to destroy me twice, would they try again? How was it that they could have this power to reach into our dimension and exert physical control? Sharma's warnings came back to me: the cobra in the basket had been aroused by the flute —and had struck. I shuddered and walked back up the beach a way, feeling the warming sun on my body, concentrating on the physical sensations that proved I was alive.

I sat in the sand and put my empty mug down beside me. The puppies were playing up in the dunes somewhere, out of sight. I lay down with my hands behind my head and closed my eyes against the sharp morning sun.

Spirits, I mused, still unconvinced, trying on

the thought for size. A spirit world, maybe beyond my control, or anyone's control. Or maybe the product of my own imagination. In either case, the only sure way to control it would be to shut it out, not think about it. Let the image die, or the entities live out their own private hells until such time as they were released. Abstract thoughts, and yet I could feel myself beginning to think of Zena as a real person, a human being asking for help. Could it help a spirit, dead nearly a century, to voice her grievances, as it sometimes did for humans to go to friends for comfort and help? I knew I could control whatever energies I felt during the séances simply by stopping. But the question was, were they in such control of me that I could not bring myself to stop? Was I already obsessed by my fascination, my curiosity? Already caught in Sharma's astral web of emotions? As I drifted off to sleep, I kept hearing my inner voice telling me to stop, to forget. But the voice was small and thin, and soon overpowered by the sound of water rushing. The sound was far away, soft, but growing louder, coming nearer, more intense. I felt an odd chill, and opened my eyes to a world of translucent gray-green, suspended somehow, touching nothing with any part of my body. I seemed to be alone, and the greenish fluid all around me was making moving shadows across my skin. I realized I was underwater, but breathing, living. Gradually, I became accustomed to the idea, and began to move tentatively. I swam a few strokes, dived a bit deeper, looked up and saw the surface of the water far above, glowing, and with a rich white spot of sun. The rushing sound was growing very loud now, and seemed to be coming from below me. I looked into the murky green darkness, toward the sound. I could see nothing. There seemed to be no bottom. And strangely, nothing alive. No fish, no seaweed, no living creature, no bubbles of air floating toward the surface. The rushing was very loud now, disturbingly loud. And within the sound I began to hear other sounds—voices. Eerie, wordless, murmuring voices, beckoning voices from the blackness below me. I became alarmed and stroked for the surface, but as I did, shadowy arms reached up and grasped at my feet and ankles. I looked down in horror at eyes—hundreds of eyes, vacant and yearning, the eyes of torment. I screamed a silent scream and stroked wildly out of reach of those arms, but they followed relentlessly, upward, now clutching at my legs, holding firmly, pulling me downward. The rushing sound was the roar of a maelstrom now, and the voices shrill and wailing. I was sucked down, down, deeper, farther from the sun. I screamed again, but my scream was soundless against the pulsing roar and the wailing, the wailing. . . .

With tremendous effort I wrenched myself away—and found myself on the beach again. The waves were crashing on the sand, and water was licking past my ankles on nearly every breaker. I sat quietly for a moment, still in the spell of the dream. Then I heard footbeats in the sand behind me, and turned to see Howard striding down the beach, a towel slung over his shoulder.

"How about a swim before breakfast?" he called. The thought of being in the ocean was like a blade of fear, but I agreed with a cheerful voice. "O.K., why not?" Howard had not been at last night's Ouija session, and I refused to allow a dream to govern my life. Howard plunged in as I pulled off my sweat shirt. I followed him into the surf, but the real cold of the water cued in a far larger chill, and I could not bring myself to dive through the waves. Howard swam swiftly. I was uncomfortable seeing him so far offshore; I knew that it was the influence of the dream, but I wanted him to come back.

"I'm going back to the house!" I shouted against the surf. "Are you coming?"

"I'll be there in a minute," he called.

"I'll start some eggs," I yelled back—and picked up my shirt and cup and went back to the house to make breakfast.

I was in a strange mood all day. People seemed to be converging on our part of the beach: Annie, who lived next door, joined us, and a girlfriend of Francois's from New York, a small, pretty, inconsequential woman whose name nobody remembered. I could not bring myself to make conversation with anyone, and found that just having people around was an irritation. I even left the puppies in the house that day. I tried reading on the beach, on the deck, in my room. I couldn't concentrate on anything; I was filled with a vague restlessness and an anxiety I could not define.

I went for a walk along the lonely stretch of dunes just to the east of The Pines. There were bizarre driftwood sculptures protruding from the sand: constructions made with railroad ties, old bottles, rusty cans, put together by artists who summered on the island. The structures looked eerie and surrealistic on the barren strip of beach, with the dunes rising beside me. I continued walking, quietly, thinking of everything and nothing. Nothing made sense, nothing was resolved, and nothing, I knew, would change.

My mood continued until evening, when Melissa arrived for dinner as planned. Just seeing her made me feel better. Those beautiful morning-glory-blue eyes fringed by their dark lashes were set off by a stunning tan. Melissa was wearing a stunning striped cotton caftan and a few pieces of massive gold jewelry. She was very New York —well educated, well read, and with a flip, gutsy sense of humor that delighted everyone. Hank was not with her, having flown to Hollywood that morning to begin work on a new film. Melissa often went out alone: She was liberated without having to be told, in full command of herself in any company, and a pleasure to have around. That evening she was particularly charming, and nobody noticed the contrast between her and François's friend more than François. He was glad to be in the kitchen, cooking. It was one of his most memorable meals: a saltimbocca, a big salad, fresh zucchini, Italian bread, and beautiful summer tomatoes. For dessert, we had fresh papaya over lime ice. The table looked wonderful, too: It was covered with a white cloth, and François had put a bowl of dune grasses in the center. After dinner we took our coffee to the living room and relaxed around the marble coffee table. The table was crowded with magazines, books, ashtrays, a few shells, and a little crystal paperweight in the shape of an egg that François had brought from somewhere. We pushed some of these things to one side to make room for the coffee tray. The glass doors to the deck were open, the curtains pulled back, and the sounds of the wind and the ocean made a dramatic background.

Melissa finished her coffee and abruptly put down her cup.

"All right," she said. "Let's get the dishes done so we can get started with the evening's activities. I'm dying to meet Beth."

It was like a bomb dropping. Everyone looked at Melissa, then at me.

"You really cannot keep your mouth shut," François whispered, his teeth clenched. He had not expected to hear about the Ouija tonight, and he had no wish to let his little socialite know about it. He was right, of course. I really could not keep my mouth shut.

"What's wrong? What's the big secret?" Melissa said.

"There's nothing wrong at all," Michael replied. Michael liked Melissa, and seemed to recognize in her the same sixth sense that he possessed, although he had not heard her story of the Union soldier. "Let's get on with it. Melissa will be all right; she'll understand." Glances of recognition passed between them.

"I don't want to do this tonight," François hissed at me. "Let's go dancing." He made a movement with his eyes toward his girl, who had begun to clear the table, totally oblivious to anything that was going on.

"What's the matter? Isn't she old enough?" Howard said.

The two women took the dishes to the kitchen and I helped them put things into the dishwasher. François's date looked confused; she had not the faintest idea what we were talking about. She folded the corners of the tablecloth together to keep the crumbs from falling, and as she bundled the cloth she saw for the first time the circle of letters on the table.

"What is this?" she said, pointing with her manicured finger.

François leaped up and snatched the cloth away from her, putting it in a disheveled heap on the table. He took her by the hand and fairly pulled her out the door. "Come on," he said. "We're going dancing." She resisted, sputtering, but he whisked her out the door, looking angrily at us over his shoulder.

Melissa was eager to get started. Howard was still sitting on the daybed, with his feet stretched out on the marble table, chuckling about François's exit. We asked him to come and take notes, and he obligingly got up and joined us. Michael checked the table, making repairs to the surface with bits of oil on a rag, and to the letters with his marker. Melissa sat with her elbows on the table, chin cupped in her hands, asking questions, fascinated. I turned out all the living-room lights and brought the candle for Michael to light. How-ard reached over and turned off the chandelier.

As the room changed from light to dark, so did the mood. Melissa became quiet, expectant, watch-ing. We all composed ourselves, breathing deeply, closing our eyes for a few moments. It was Me-lissa's first séance, and our first time with a strang-er participating. I could feel the difference in our state of mind: It took a little longer to remove the layer of self-consciousness that we all felt. After a few moments, when I felt more relaxed, I looked across at Michael. Together, we touched the glass with our fingers, then looked at Melissa, who did the same. The glass spiraled around the alphabet with incredible speed, but smoothly, waiting for a question.

"Is that you, Zena?" I asked. The energy was positive and effortless, and, if anything, stronger than it had felt the previous night.

YES ZENA

"Why didn't Beth help you and others aboard the ship?"

THEY DID NOT HELP ONLY THEMSELVES ALL BE-LOW LOST

"Did they drown later?"

EVENTUALLY

"When?"

1878 ROSAMOND NOT MINE BETHS CHILD

There was a quick, changing pattern of energies, and the glass faltered around the board. I knew Beth's presence by now. Melissa shivered in the sudden chill.

I AM MAKING IT WARMER   A pause, struggling. LAUGH RELIEF FOR ME

Another struggle, and then the smooth energy we recognized as Zena's:

NOTHING BUT BETHS INFLUENCE SHE HAD NO IDEA TRUTH WOULD BE TOLD TOLD LIVING

The glass paused as Howard took it all down, deciphered it, and read us the message. Then it began again.

IN YOUR GAME YOU HAD NO IDEA THAT NEW FRIEND WOULD BE MADE   I WAIT MORE TO TELL

The energy was strong, but the conflict was very evident to us. Michael looked furtively from me to Melissa, unable to concentrate on the board as he usually did. The glass moved falteringly.

BETH

"Is it Beth?"

YES

Another struggle: I felt the growing irritation I had experienced the first time Beth had gained control of our séance. Then the energy smoothed out again.

BETH IS NOT GONE HERE NOW BETH IS AFRAID

The glass pulled violently to one side of the table, away from the letters. Melissa could not reach it until it moved back and haltingly spelled out its message.

It took longer for Howard to decipher Beth's messages: They always were filled with doubled letters and misspellings, and the atmosphere we wished for, one of serene concentration, was impossible to sustain. Melissa shifted uneasily, waiting for Howard to read the message.

DO NOT FEAR ME BETH

The glass moved again, smoothly, and so fast it was difficult for us to keep up with it.

I CAN CONTROL HER   SHES ALL OVER   A struggle, then a smooth flow.   IT WAS THE LAST TIME BETH IS NOT HERE EVER AGAIN   But we felt the stutter of Beth's energy, and knew she was still present. The glass rushed from letter to letter, but the message was so jumbled that it was impossible for Howard to make any sense of it at all.

He looked up and shook his head. The glass moved again:

LAST TIME   BETH SPEAKS FOR LAST TIME NOT ME BUT BETH   The flow was clearly back to normal now. I waited a few seconds as the glass circled the letters, and then resumed the questioning.

"Who is here?"

ZENA   ASK ME

"How did the ship sink?"

FIRE   LIVERPOOL MANY WEEKS ON THE SEA

"What work did you do?"

CUTTERS MILL

"Why did you choose us to tell your story to?"

YOU CALLED ME   YOU OPENED DOOR TO OCEAN
BETH CAN KNOW WHO IS WEAK   SHE CAN POSSESS
I felt Melissa's eyes on me.

"We understand. Why should we fear her?"

BECAUSE BETH WAS PRESENT   SHE DOES NOT
WANT ME TO TELL TRUTH   I CAME TO PROTECT
YOU   NONE OF YOU NEED FEAR AS LONG AS I AM
HERE

"What about outside the house?"

DANGEROUS TO GO IN THE WATER ALONE   BETH
IS EVIL   ROSAMOND AND ALL DEAD BECAUSE OF
BETH

"Why because of Beth only?"

SHE COULD HAVE SAVED US BUT DID NOT   SHE
DID NOT WANT US   SHE CAN CAUSE SHIPWRECKS

"You mean she has been the cause of the destruction of other ships?"

1919   BECAUSE OF BETH   BETH IS CALCULAT-
ING

"How can she cause such things to happen?"

SHE CAN BE EVIL   SHE CAN POSSESS   SARA-
TOGA   1919

"Was Saratoga the name of a ship?"

YES   IN THE SEA NEAR MY GRAVE   BETH IS RE-
SPONSIBLE   BETH IS FAR MORE ALONE   I WILL
SPEAK MORE TONIGHT   REST FOR TEN

The energy stopped. We rested, knowing it
would continue. I remained silent, using the time
to refocus my concentration. At the end of ten
minutes we touched the glass, which immediately
began rapidly and smoothly to move without wait-

ing for a question. It was a long message and we waited quietly for Howard to figure it out.

ALL UPSET   ALL AFRAID   BETH IS CAPABLE OF HARM   THAT IS WHY YOU ARE UPSET AND AFRAID BETH IS EVIL   BUT I KNOW ALL THE TRUTH AS YOU DO NOW   THE ONLY IMPORTANCE IS MY TRUTH TO YOU

"Is she here now?"

NOT NOW   SEA   SHE IS IN THE SEA

"Is the wreck still there?"

WRECK STILL THERE   IS COLD THERE

"Is it cold here?"

WARM BECAUSE OF ME   I WILL WATCH FOR ANYTHING   I AM HERE ONLY TO PROTECT YOU   I WILL BE HERE WHEN YOU WANT ME

The energy ceased abruptly, and we knew it would not begin again.

Melissa slumped back in her chair as if she had been released from a magnetic hold. Her blue eyes were huge; it was obvious that she had been thoroughly shaken by the experience. "Incredible," was all she could say. "Utterly incredible." She wanted to hear everything again, with all the details we could remember. She was full of questions, and listened seriously to everything, including all the possible theories about the phenomena we were dealing with, and all that Sharma had told us. It was good to have Melissa there, asking questions, making us examine ourselves. She wanted to know what I had learned in the library, and everything that we felt and thought about what was happening here. I told her about the car accident, and since Howard had not been with us the night before to hear the threat, Michael filled them in on that.

The idea that the spirits could attach themselves to you and travel with you wherever you went met with great resistance from Howard, who was positive neither my near-drowning nor the accident had to do with anything but circumstances.

"But we're not imagining these messages," said Melissa.

Howard shook his head. "There's got to be some rational explanation."

I had narrowed the possibilities down to three: Either we were getting psychic feedback from a past life, as Michael had suggested; or there were indeed spirits in the otherworld who were trying to communicate with us; or I was insane. And if I was insane, we all were.

"This thing is really getting to you," Howard said. "So what if there are spirits? Let them be. Is it really worth it to put yourself through this?" He got up from his chair and tossed the pencil onto the table. "It's not a game anymore, it's an obsession with you. Why don't you just quit? Look at the way you're ruining your summer. We've been here three weekends and you haven't gone out once so far. You've hardly visited any of your friends, you're moody during the day, and now you're even afraid to go swimming."

"But look at how the story is developing!" said Michael. "Every night we find out something more, a little more information that ties in with the rest. Zena is desperately trying to get help of some kind."

"You're insane," said Howard. He went into the living room and fell heavily into a sofa.

"But how can *we* help?" I asked Michael. It was exactly the same problem I had tried to come to grips with on the beach that morning. "Perhaps the very idea that we can help her is her own delusion. And ours. And if Beth is evil and treacherous, how far do we want to stick our necks out to help Zena—what risks do we want to take?"

"You can't even know what risks are possible," Howard called out. "Give it up, before you really do drive yourselves crazy." Michael paid no attention. He was studying the notes of the evening.

"Look at this!" he said. "All the struggle between Zena and Beth. It looks to me as if Beth has been torturing her sister for all these years—and now Zena is trying to make up for it, to take advantage of her contact with us for some purpose of her own."

"Yes," I agreed. "It seems somehow important to Zena that the truth be told to the living. Some weapon against Beth. Some power."

"Did you notice how much stronger the energy was tonight?" Michael asked. I had noticed. Perhaps our resistance to Beth's intrusions gave support to Zena, and allowed her to grow stronger. She seemed able to stay longer. Or perhaps Melissa's presence added the extra energy.

I had other questions—questions I knew could

never be answered: By what power did one spirit control another? What spiritual or emotional chains did Zena use to bind Beth away from us—and by what power did Beth free herself to come and interfere again? Was it, as Zena said, safe for us? Would Zena be able to continue to hold Beth in check? Melissa wanted to know how we could be so sure that Zena herself was not a threat to us. But Michael was convinced that Zena would do us no harm.

"You can feel the difference in the energy flow," he said, "and the kinds of things she says—it's clear she has good intentions. I think she had something important to tell us."

I was still puzzling over the spirits' interactions with one another and with our world. We were locked in our own three-dimensional world, and the power that allowed us to receive their messages by this mysterious circle of letters was a puzzle in itself. We could not see them, yet apparently they could not only see us, but hear our words and even our thoughts. Still more baffling, they could cause people to drown, ships to sink, perhaps even cars to crash. How? Where did they get this power?

"You'll never know that," said Howard. "Look, a series of events took place. Who knows why? The current is bad out there. People have drowned without the help of ghosts. And people have had car accidents, too."

"Those were not coincidences," said Michael with sobering finality. "Arnold nearly drowned and was brought to this very house. Things fit to-gether too tightly. And if we are all in danger, as the spirit says, it would be wise for you, even if you don't believe it, not to swim out too far."

But something else was at work here. Some-thing besides the possibility of spirits or imagina-tion, or whether we could or could not force our-selves to stop. I thought back to Sharma's explana-tion of the astral realm, and what I had read in my book about reincarnation. Here were bodyless souls that could not rest. Zena died tragically, with the shame and torment of having been wrongly blamed for bringing a fatherless child into the world. Now dead, she was still living out the shame that had filled her whole being. To her, she was only an image of shame and anger and hatred and frustration. This was the image she was living now, in death. This was her illusion. It was like a neurosis that becomes the focus of a human life. We, the living, all have our own illusions that we live with until we die, and most of us do not ever realize it. I understood this, and could not help feeling sympathy for this poor woman.

If all this was true, if people in death lived illu-sions of their own making, then Zena's illusion was becoming our illusion as well. Howard sug-gested that it was our own illusion to begin with, and it may well have been. Layers of illusion, in-tertangling the threads of Zena's being, whatever she was, and our own.

SEVENTH ENCOUNTER

Friday, July 21

Melissa must have called me a dozen times that week. She was incredibly excited about the Ouija, and thought it absolutely fabulous that we were able to do such a thing. She didn't waste any time on self-doubt, questioning, or trepidation. Her enthusiasm was complete; her excitement recharged my own. It wasn't so much that she accepted the Ouija as proof of the existence of a netherworld; she knew that as intuitively as Sharma did, although not with the aloof coolness and cautious reserve. It was that she seemed to feel a personal kind of affinity for anything spiritual and supernatural: She was enamored of the whole concept, and of the fact that she had been involved in it. She couldn't wait to get back to the Ouija the following weekend.

When I told her that we might not be able to

continue with the Ouija because I was worried about François, her reaction shocked me. She became merciless.

"Buy him out," she said ruthlessly. "You've accomplished something few people, if any, have ever been able to do. You've contacted the same spirits week after week and learned stories that make sense. How can you let anyone stand in your way?"

Some friends of mine from England were in town that week, and since I knew that Hank was still in Los Angeles working on a film, I invited Melissa to join us for dinner one evening. She accepted at once. She told me that Hank would be returning in a couple of weeks, and that a good friend of ours, actor Robert Chambers, who was then working on a new film, would also be coming.

I invited Sharma to dinner, too. Sharma and Melissa liked each other very much, although their personalities were completely opposite on the surface. They seemed to share some common kinship on a deeper level. When I told Sharma about Melissa's enthusiastic reaction to the Ouija, she was not surprised, nor was she particularly worried. She smiled at what she called Melissa's fools-rush-in personality, but said fearlessness would most likely protect her. We went to a French restaurant, a little out-of-the-way spot in the West Fifties. One of my English friends, Pamela, whose mother was one of J. Paul Getty's official hostesses in London, had nevertheless come penniless to New York because of British currency regulations, and had to make regular trips to an office on Wall Street to borrow money. The two men, whose situations were not so outrageous, had typically British offbeat senses of humor, counterbalanced by Melissa's gutsy New York wisecracking. We laughed throughout the entire meal.

There was, of course, no way the subject of the Ouija could be avoided as long as Melissa was in the group. She could scarcely talk of anything else, and my English friends were eager to hear more. Melissa painted such an exciting picture of the one session she had experienced that Pamela insisted we all go back to her room and try to contact some spirits there. I was reluctant, but the combined enthusiasm of Melissa and Pamela persuaded me (Sharma was completely aloof as usual, although her eyes cautioned me). Pamela was staying at Ben Sonnenberg's house on Grammercy Park. She and the others thought it would be a great place to have a séance.

We paid the check, crammed ourselves into a Checker taxi, and headed across town. None of the Sonnenberg family was about, and Pamela thought it just as well that they did not know we were there. Stealthily we snooped around, being careful not to arouse the servants. Ben Sonnenberg was a very well-known promotion man who had practically founded the public-relations business. He had worked for political figures and theater people, and had fabulous collections of theater memorabilia. The kitchen looked as if it were in a hotel: two huge rooms—one a pantry, one where the actual cooking took place—all stainless steel and spotlessly sterile. Pamela opened a cupboard filled with crystal, from which I selected a small juice glass as close as possible in size and weight to the one we used at Fire Island.

What fascinated me most were the telephones. There were at least a dozen extension lines, and under each telephone was a laminated card that listed the various numbers where Mr. Sonnenberg could be reached: Mr. Sonnenberg's study; Mr. Sonnenberg's bath; Mr. Sonnenberg's bedroom; Mr. Sonnenberg's library—the list went on.

"Come in," Pamela whispered. We got into the small elevator that took us upstairs to her room.

There we cleared a small table. Someone produced a felt-tip pen with which I drew a Ouija like the one we had on the Island. We arranged ourselves around the table—all except Sharma, who again would have nothing to do with it. My heart was not in it either. I hadn't asked anyone to bring a candle; the room, I told Melissa, was dark enough. There was no invocation. We merely sat around the table with our fingers on the glass. Melissa asked questions, and so did the others from time to time. I felt no energy; the glass remained motionless. We sat there for nearly an hour, and I felt as if I were perpetrating some kind of fraud. I really did not want to contact any spirits and, if indeed there were any spirits in the vicinity, I was sure my negative impulse would have kept them from contacting us. Finally we agreed that to try any longer was useless. Melissa and Pamela were disappointed, Sharma relieved. The two men were unaffected either way, since they had been curious but skeptical to begin with.

But I learned something from the experience. Or rather I became conscious of something I must have known intuitively: It was not the Ouija board itself that held the power, but the people who operated it. The Ouija may have attracted spirits, as Sharma had warned us, but the phenomenon of actually contacting the spirit world had something to do with will—and more than will, with serious intent. During our sessions at The Pines, there were two of us who concentrated, who wished for contact, who willingly opened ourselves to receive the energies. And one who, through his fear, opened himself unwittingly. I began to see that the interaction of the human and the supernatural worlds hinged on some form of energy generated in both worlds simultaneously, and that, without both mechanisms engaged, no knowable contact could be made. I could not begin to explain such an idea but I knew intuitively that there was something to it.

I also recognized that, logically, this idea was open to strong intellectual criticism, including my own on the very first night we had begun to explore the Ouija. I had said that if one wanted badly enough for something to happen, one might imagine that it actually did. Yet now, having experienced the phenomenon myself, I began to realize what a nebulous thing reality can be. Had I, inexperienced at the Ouija, heard my own story from some stranger, I would probably have listened with curiosity, and then dismissed it for any number of intellectual or psychological reasons. But I had actually experienced it myself, with a number of other people, and no matter how many incredulous questions my mind raised, intuitively I could not dismiss it.

Before my friends went back to England, they asked me when I would be coming over. "How about later this summer?" Pamela asked. "You can stay with me." I thanked her, but told her I really couldn't make any plans right now.

On Thursday, I took a day off from my work and went back to the library to check on the added information Zena had given us the weekend before. *Saratoga*, 1919, was uppermost on my mind. Now with the name of a ship and a relatively recent date, I thought I must be able to find something on record. The sky was very gray and overcast when I left the house; I took along my umbrella. I rode the Seventh Avenue subway to the Forty-Second Street station and walked two blocks to the main library. Up in the records room, the librarian nodded a silent greeting. I filled out slips for the shipwreck-disaster books I had found on my previous visit and searched for the *Saratoga*. There it was: the *Saratoga*, whose wreck off the Long Island coast had caused the deaths of eighteen persons in addition to the captain—but it had happened much earlier than

1919. I frowned and sat back, disappointed. I searched for a few more hours. In the year 1919, there were several ships lost, but none named *Saratoga*. It occurred to me that it might have been a smaller boat, too small to have been recorded. It might be worthwhile to come back another day to check further, I thought. But I had had enough for today. I took the books back to the desk and walked down the marble stairs. Outside, it was pouring rain. The sky was slate gray and thunderclaps exploded directly overhead. My umbrella was practically useless in the strong wind as I picked my way carefully down the slippery stone steps and out into the street. Not a vacant taxi in sight on Forty-Second Street or Fifth Avenue. I pulled my collar up, ran to the subway station and took a train home, soaking wet.

The next afternoon I had to take the train to Sayville. François had made other plans for the weekend, so only Michael, Howard, and I were at the house. And my two puppies, who were always with me. Melissa had gone out on Thursday to Water Island, and we expected her to arrive at our place after dinner. When she arrived it was late afternoon; Howard and I were still on the beach. We were surprised to see her husband, Hank, with her; he must have returned early from Hollywood. I half expected to see Robert Chambers sauntering up behind them, but Hank laughed and said that Bob was still wrapping up his film and would be out as scheduled in a couple of weeks. Hank himself had to go back out to the coast to finish his own film, but had decided to take a break and spend a few days in New York.

Although Melissa and Hank had not been expected for dinner, their early arrival caused no problem. Howard had been planning to go out for the evening, and Michael intended to make a very simple meal: an omelette and a salad. A few extra eggs made no difference to him. I brought out some wine and we relaxed for a while on the deck before dinner.

Melissa wanted to know what I had discovered at the library, and I told them all just what I had found: nothing that could be construed as evidence. Michael looked thoughtful, and went to fetch the notes from the last couple of weekends.

"Wait a minute," he said. "What if Zena didn't mean 1919 to be a date? She often repeats herself. What if it was 19. 19. Perhaps nineteen was the number of shipwrecks Beth caused."

"Or," said Howard, "maybe it was the number of people lost in the *Saratoga* wreck. Didn't you say eighteen people lost, plus the captain?" I looked at him in amazement. Could that be it? 19. 19. I was thunderstruck. I determined to ask Zena tonight.

Michael and Melissa fixed dinner together, and I concocted the vinaigrette for the salad. Michael and I both were fairly good cooks, but neither of us had the kind of passion about it that François had. Tonight cooking became a community activity, with everyone in the kitchen helping or keeping company. Hank was full of stories from the movie business out on the coast, and kept us laughing all through dinner. When the time came to clear things away and begin the Ouija, Hank, who had never been to a séance, was full of wisecracks. Melissa shot him a reprimanding look. They had apparently talked about it before they came.

We gathered ourselves around the table in the darkened room. Michael ritualistically prepared the table and saw to the lights. No one spoke during the preparations except Hank, and our silence soon made him aware of a change in our attitude. He sat quietly and watched, more out of consideration for us than anything else. I brought the yellow pad and asked Hank if he would take notes this evening, explaining our procedure. He agreed. Melissa, Michael, and I touched our fingers to the glass, and immediately there was a strong rush of energy. The force of the energy was like nothing I had felt before, uninterrupted, smooth. It seemed to fill my whole body with a strange charge.

BETH IS HERE YES NO

"Are you both here?" I asked.

YES

Somehow I felt we were not dealing with Zena at all. I decided to try to get some real information from Beth. Perhaps with our understanding she, too, could be helped.

141

"Is there another spirit here with you, Beth?"

YES

"Beth, what do you have to say?"

YOU FIND OUT HOW STRONG I AM IN MY TIME YOU ARE IN FOR MORE A pause. IN MY TIME WHY DO YOU INTERFERE WITH US

There was a fearful jerk on the board, and the glass was wrenched from one side to the other as we all struggled to keep our fingers near it, if not actually on it. Hank deciphered the parts of the message we could not understand as they were being given, and read it to us. I started to ask another question, but the glass moved first. We followed it with our fingers and eyes.

HIGGINS I CAN DESTROY ALL HIGGINS

Higgins! Could this be yet another spirit—the Higgins Zena dreaded? Where was Zena? Had Beth and Higgins conspired against her once again? Was she not free of their torment even in her grave?

"What do you want?" I asked angrily.

DO NOT INTERFERE YOU WILL FEEL MORE TO-NIGHT WHEN I WANT NO MORE I CAN BE MORE THAN YOU WANT NO MORE

The energy when Higgins wrote was alarmingly strong and smooth, much more so even than Zena's had been. And apparently under the protection of her captain and lover, Beth could contact us with a smoother flow of energy. It must have been Zena's preventive measures that short-circuited Beth's energy on previous nights. I was disquieted by the power of this new spirit, but made a conscious effort to steel myself, to remain detached and strong.

"What about Zena?" I asked. "She can control you. And we will not let you do any harm to us."

LEAVE ZENA WITH US

"Beth, tell us what you want," I said. I sensed that Beth was under this man's control, and that perhaps we could encourage her by allowing her a voice of her own. Besides, if Beth had a story to tell, without Zena's interference we might hear and learn from it.

NO WE CAN STOP ALL THIS

"How? Is this a threat?"

YOU WILL SEE IN MY TIME

"Tell us your story then."

NOTHING TO TELL

"Is what Zena told us true?"

NO

I had been doing all the questioning, with Michael and Melissa watching, both wide-eyed, absorbed in the Ouija and its revelations. Now Melissa's eyes narrowed, and she became impatient with Beth.

"I don't believe you," she said. "Go away from us and stop telling lies." No, Melissa, I thought to myself. You'll ruin everything.

MELISSA KNOWS ALL I CAN STOP HER

"I am too strong for you," Melissa said, challenged. "You will never succeed."

The glass spun around the letters in a fury of

speed, spelling out vicious, vile insults against Melissa.

WHORE CUNT FUCKING BITCH

"You think you can scare me with your filth?" Melissa shouted, enraged. "You are filthy and weak. You can never hurt me."

FUCKING WHORE WHICH COCK WILL YOU FUCK TONIGHT BIG COCK NOT HERE HOWARD FUCK HOWARD FUCKING CUNT

Hank was so shocked that he couldn't read the message out loud. We had been able to read as the glass sped around the board, and we were all dumbfounded at the obscenities. Hank stopped writing altogether and became very protective of Melissa. But she would have none of it. She had read the message with the rest of us. "Filthy bitch!" she shouted. At that moment the heavy glass ashtray with the lighted candle lifted itself off the table and hurled itself at Melissa. There was a cry and the crash of glass against the opposite wall.

I sat bolt upright in the blackness. Everything had happened in the splitting of a second; there was no time even to think. No one spoke. At last somebody found the light switch.

"Are you all right, Melissa?" I asked. She was sitting with one elbow on the table, fingering a thread of blood where the ashtray had grazed her forehead. She was not crying, but her eyes were full of an alarming mixture of terror and hatred.

"Everything is fine," she said in a soft, controlled voice.

Hank was instantly at her side. "Good God," he said. Michael and I could not find suitable words.

"I'm so terribly sorry," I said lamely. "Nothing like this has ever happened before." Hank did not answer. He took Melissa over to the daybed and had her lie down while Michael got a washcloth with some cool water. We all sat around the living room, trying to break the atmosphere by talking about other things. But no conversation could be sustained, and the long intervals of uneasy silence were discomforting.

"Come on," said Hank again. "Let's go down to the village."

We walked along the narrow boardwalk in the dark, silent night. The air was very clear and the sight of the dense white stars had a cleansing, comforting effect on me and I suspect on us all. We walked single file and close to one another, realizing how much we had been affected.

In the smoky lights and din of the Boatel, where rock music blared, we threaded our way across the room filled with bodies heaving to the pulsing rhythms and found a table out on the deck where it was quieter. A waiter took our order and brought us drinks. We sat together, hardly speaking at all, protected and comforted by the masses of people all around. At last someone dared to bring up what we had all seen that night, and what no one had yet acknowledged in words.

"How did it happen?" Michael said. "My God, how did it happen?"

We had all seen it. The whole ashtray and candle had flung itself across the table using no energy that could be explained in human terms. My head began to spin again with the significance of what we had just come through. These entities had proved that they could wield real physical power and, even more alarming, with a speed and force that made it impossible to prevent. Moreover, although their power was real, the source was invisible, making them a formidable enemy.

The other discovery was the language that was used by the spirit. Never had we witnessed such vicious or obscene transmissions before. Was it because Zena had been protecting us from these two evil spirits, whom we all now thought of as monsters?

But most awesome to me was the terrible fight between the living woman and the dead one. It was almost like a rivalry. We could feel Beth's jealousy of Melissa: her beauty, her obvious sex appeal, and above all, her ability to perform the act that Beth, in death, could only imagine, the act for which she had died and endured so much suffering.

What I could not understand was Melissa's deep involvement in the quarrel. Beth certainly was not a physical rival. It had to be something else, some spiritual kinship Melissa felt that drew her into the dark circle. No one had to tell me how dangerous this was, not after what had happened tonight. I still was determined to go on with the sessions as long as we could, but I also knew that we could not have a repeat performance of this.

I tried to explain to Melissa how dangerous it was to allow herself to be carried away by the séances. She nodded her head in agreement.

"I know it," she said. "I just couldn't seem to help myself. I won't let it happen again."

"You won't have a chance to let it happen again," Hank said flatly and without humor. "Tonight was enough."

"We'll talk about it when we're alone," Melissa said wearily.

Hank took me aside and asked why I didn't just call the whole thing off. But at this point I would not be deterred. To me the whole evening had been as much a revelation as a warning.

"With every séance we learn a little more," I told him. "But we don't know yet everything we need to know, and we must go on as long as possible." I told him I thought the shocking involvement between Melissa and Beth was caused as much by Melissa's affinity to the spiritual and her own inability to remain detached as by any innate power the spirits possessed. Hank bristled and would have protested, but I stopped him.

"It's nothing against Melissa," I said quickly. "She's very psychic—and seems to have this natural affinity. Michael has very much the same thing. She simply must learn to control her emotions and not let herself become involved—the spirits feed on emotional energy."

"She doesn't have to change anything," he said in a whisper, "because I won't allow her to be part of this crazy business again."

"As you wish," I said. "I certainly can understand how you feel." We returned to the others. I wished Sharma were there. I had the creeping suspicion that the power we had observed was only the tip of the iceberg, and that the unseen world might actually be the cause of more insanity, physical attacks, and deaths in the world than anyone had suspected. Once an entity from the astral plane got a foothold in your life, what powers could it siphon from your own energies? And, I thought ominously, I was sure that the Ouija was not the only key that unlocked the physical world to these beings. What other doors do humans open between the two dimensions, unwittingly inviting unexplained, frighteningly real disasters? The talk continued around the table, but I did not participate. I was deep in my own thoughts, and all else was lost in the din of drums and reverberating electronic instruments pulsing through the black night air. I watched the closely packed, gyrating, sweating human bodies, then turned my eyes to the deck, to the dark water whose gentle moving pattern reflected the vast, cold, star-filled sky.

EIGHTH ENCOUNTER

Saturday, July 22

The first thing I wanted when I woke up the next morning was a cold shower. Howard's bed was already made, and the sun was too high to see from my window. I felt the pleasant humid warmth of the summer morning and concentrated on it with contentment. I looked at the clock: eleven thirty. I pulled on my shorts and headed for the bathroom, only to find it in use. The kettle was boiling on the kitchen stove, so I made a pot of coffee. On the table was a note from Howard: He had gone water-skiing and would not reappear until just before dinner. So it must be Michael in the shower. Presently he emerged, wrapped in a towel, and joined me in the kitchen for coffee and toast.

"What are your plans for the day?" he asked me, sipping hot coffee while he rubbed his head with the towel in his other hand.

"None whatever," I said flatly. I wanted to go out on the beach, lie in the sun, rest, and above all not have to socialize with anyone. Michael apparently felt the same way, so we had our breakfast and spent the rest of the day relaxing. In fact there was only one interruption: Sometime during the afternoon I was brought out of a pleasant half sleep on the beach by the touch of cool fingers on my shoulder. I looked up to see Melissa, brown and slippery with oil, wearing a black bikini and a batik sarong tied artlessly around her hips. Her face as she leaned over me was framed by her mane of hair. She looked sensational.

"Go back to sleep," she said quietly. "I just wanted to tell you that I'll see you tonight." She smiled and, without waiting for an answer, stood up and continued her walk down the beach.

I smiled to myself: I could imagine what poor Hank must have gone through the night before, trying to convince Melissa that coming back for tonight's session would be dangerous. The woman didn't know the meaning of the word. I turned over on my stomach and drifted off to sleep.

Howard showed up just as Michael and I were gathering the beach towels and heading back to the house at the end of the afternoon. We all were feeling a little hungry, so I thought I'd put a salad together to tide us over until dinner that evening. Howard and Michael decided to have one final swim before coming inside. I walked back to the house alone. Annie was out on her deck as I passed on my way to our own. She greeted me with a wave, which I returned.

"By the way," she said, "whatever it is you're doing over there at night, I sure wish you'd stop. I'm having a lot of trouble sleeping." I stopped in my tracks. If she knew about the Ouija, she didn't let on. I thought perhaps we had been making noise, but that couldn't be it. For all the excitement of the Ouija, it was conducted in fairly hushed tones.

"We aren't being too noisy, are we?" I asked good-humoredly.

"Oh no," she said quickly. "It's not noise that's keeping me awake. But something else, and I feel sure it's coming from your place." She stopped and shrugged. "Having said that, now I feel foolish," she said laughing. "Perhaps a cup of hot tea before retiring would cure my insomnia."

I had not really thought about the Ouija all day, except momentarily when Melissa stopped by. Annie's complaint brought it all to the front of my mind, and I wondered again about the scope and range of the spirits' influence. True, Annie's house was so close to ours that we could almost touch its shingled siding from our deck. Their house was thrust forward of ours, however, so our decks were completely private. Her bedroom was near our dining area. But still, I couldn't see how a person in an area removed from us could come under the influence of the forces we were dealing with, whatever they were.

That evening Howard, Michael, and I whipped some dinner together and ate out on the deck. Michael and I told Howard what had happened the night before. He got a chuckle out of Beth's reference to his being well hung, and thought that the interchanges between Melissa and Beth were in keeping with Melissa's aggressive nature. He still felt sure that somehow we ourselves were responsible for all the phenomena that had taken place. As for the ashtray and candle that had flown across the room, I could see that he just couldn't believe it. When someone describes an event out of the range of ordinary experience, one is hard pressed to accept it as truth, and this was exactly Howard's situation. I understood. Michael and I could scarcely believe it ourselves, and we had witnessed it, together with two other people.

Just as we were getting ready for coffee, Melissa arrived—accompanied by Hank. There was no talk of whether or not to have our session that evening: Everyone knew what Hank and Melissa had come for, and if Hank was less than pleased about it, he kept quiet. I took our trays back to the kitchen and put some coffee on while the others talked together out on the deck. The sun had gone down long before, and the deck was lighted only by the lamps shining out through the windows. The breaking of the waves made a restful, rhythmic background.

I suddenly felt very tired. The day in the sun was draining, although I had done hardly anything but sleep. My skin was sunburned, and was beginning to be uncomfortable. The breeze made me shiver, and I suggested we take our cups to the living room where it would be warmer. Nobody hurried to finish coffee, and not a word was spoken about the séance that was to follow, or the one the evening before. I noticed a kind of forced casualness in Hank's voice whenever he spoke, but everyone else seemed very relaxed. I rubbed my sunburned knee with one hand, and pressed my fingers into the skin, watching the white mark it made dissolve into the original redness. I knew I'd feel it the next day.

It was very late when we finished coffee and cleared the things away. While Melissa and I took care of that operation, Michael removed the cloth from the table and set up the Ouija.

We arranged ourselves around the table, Howard with the yellow pad, Hank, protectively, slightly behind Melissa. She, Michael, and I would be the participants tonight.

The glass began moving just as we touched it. The surge of energy was almost exhilarating in an eerie way. I had a feeling there was more than one spirit present: and moreover, that they were working in cooperation. When Beth and Zena were at odds, their conflict manifested itself in halting, maddening struggles on the board; the evening before, however, when Beth and Higgins had been unencumbered by Zena's presence, we had felt just this strong, gripping charge of energy.

MELISSA RETURNS

"Who are you?" I asked.

HOWARD HERE TOO MELISSA KNOWS FUCKING WHORE

I glanced at Melissa; she was biting her lip, knowing she should not become involved. The glass continued to move steadily in a circle around the letters, waiting for a question.

"Where is Zena?" I asked.

ZENA NO LONGER NO MORE ZENA GONE

"We are bored with you, Beth," I said. "We will talk only to Zena. Leave us now."

I AM NOT A CHILD DO NOT PLAY GAMES WITH US NEVER AGAIN ZENA YOU TRESPASS NO MORE ZENA

"We are not afraid of your threats," I insisted. "Leave us. Let us talk to Zena." There was a pause for about a minute, and then a terrific jerking surge of power as the glass wrenched itself from one side of the table to the other. Then we felt the smooth, steady flow we had come to recognize as Zena's:

DO NOT FEAR THEY CANNOT HURT ANY OF YOU I STOP THEM

"Zena. Can we help you?"

YES DO NOT ALLOW THEM   A struggle on the board. I CANNOT REMAIN Another struggle, and then the strong power we had felt at first, ominous and foreboding.

ZENA FLIES IN FEAR HIGGINS STRONGER LAUGH FOR ZENA

"Where has Zena gone?" I demanded. I had an uneasy feeling that Zena was no match for Higgins and Beth combined. The only way I could think of to help her was to resist them with all my might. "Bring Zena to us. We do not wish to talk with you."

ZENA GONE BETH HIGGINS HAVE POWER YOU WILL DO AS WE WANT

"We are not afraid of you."

MELISSA FEARS YOU FEAR HANK FEARS MICHAEL FEARS HIGGINS WILL DESTROY ALL

Melissa could not keep still. "I am not afraid of any of you," she said haughtily.

MELISSA FUCKING CUNT BITCH

"You jealous filthy witch," Melissa shouted. "I am stronger than you."

"Melissa!" I said, and Hank put a hand on her shoulder. But she would not be calmed. She shouted as the glass moved from letter to letter, spelling its obscenities. Her eyes were wild. Behind Michael, the dishwasher door began slamming open and shut, open and shut. Melissa shouted above the clatter, out of her mind with rage.

"Stop it Melissa!" I shouted above her. "Ignore them. Don't let yourself . . ." Melissa's huge eyes glared at me, and her hand swung around and struck me hard in the face. I lurched back, stung.

Everything stopped. Melissa wrenched back into her chair as if she had been struggling to be released. Hank's arms were instantly around her. Her eyes were wide, her mouth limp with shock and shame. She put her hands to her face.

"I'm sorry," she said quietly, beginning to cry. "I'm so sorry." Everyone was silent. I felt furious at Melissa for slapping me, and even more than that, for losing control of herself a second time.

Then the fury turned to remorse, and I felt the burden of my own responsibility. I was tired, and very drained.

The others decided they needed a change of scene. Hank wanted to get Melissa away from the house, and I agreed that it would surely be best. But I was simply too exhausted to go out.

"You go ahead," I said wearily. "I am going to sleep." This night had been too much for me. Melissa caught hold of my hand as I passed her on the way to my bedroom. I stopped and looked down at her, and took a long breath. I squeezed her shoulder and smiled as best I could.

As I slowly prepared for bed, I could hear the sounds of the others' voices as they prepared to leave. Then the door closed, and their voices drifted farther and farther away as they progressed down the boardwalk on their way to the discotheque.

I opened my bedroom curtains so that I could see the sky, got into bed, and turned out the light. I was exhausted—too exhausted to fall asleep—and I lay awake thinking in the blackness. Gradually as I lay there the room began to reappear as my eyes became accustomed to the grayish haze of night. I lay in the stillness, listening to the sound of the ceaseless ocean, letting my thoughts follow themselves through my brain, when suddenly everything inside me froze.

There was something at the foot of my bed. It felt as if someone had come and sat down on the end of the mattress. I could feel that the whole corner had been pressed down, tightening the sheet across my feet. I did not move, but looked down with my eyes toward the foot end. The bed was indeed depressed, but *there was no one there.* I forced myself not to be afraid. I lay calmly, not moving a muscle. If it was Zena, I told myself, I had nothing to fear. If it was Beth, or Higgins, I was not about to give them the satisfaction of showing they could frighten me. I deliberately filled myself with strength; I detached myself from the whole event, and merely observed. About thirty seconds later the end of my bed rose by itself to its normal position. I continued to watch for another few minutes, measuring my breaths, then relaxed and drifted off to sleep.

The next week, a check from the insurance company arrived in the mail. The first thing I did was call the Mercedes people and make an appointment to look at cars. I picked out a 220 SL, navy blue with white leather interior. I wrote a check for the full amount. The next afternoon, the car was delivered.

I felt like a teenager with his first souped-up convertible. I hurried to finish some work, ran downstairs, and just sat in the car, admiring the wood dashboard, smelling the new leather. It was silly just to sit there by myself; I had to go for a ride. I turned on the ignition and took off for Sharma's place. I left the engine running and ran up to her apartment two steps at a time to see if she was home. She was busily going over some

music for a new ballet she was helping to choreo-
graph, but I had no trouble snatching her away.
We drove happily down the West Side Highway
from Nineteenth Street, all around the lower end
of Manhattan, and then up along the East River
and across the northern end of the city, then down
again along the Hudson. The air was warm and
clear except for a band of purple haze across the
lower part of the sky. We decided to celebrate with
dinner at Casey's, a posh watering hole on West
Tenth Street in the Village where Andy Warhol,
Norman Mailer, and other celebrities sometimes
hung out.

We toasted my new car with champagne and
had a good time talking and saying hello to friends
we saw across the crowded room. Eventually, I
told Sharma about the preceding weekend and
what had happened to Melissa. Sharma's first reaction was genuine surprise. But she quickly realized the danger of Melissa's involvement. At first
she had thought Melissa's strength would save
her, but now she was not so sure. It was one
thing for the ashtray and the dishwasher door to
be moved by the spirits. But for Melissa herself
to strike me was an act that could not be dismissed. Sharma was sure the spirits were responsible, and might actually have taken control of
Melissa for that brief second. It was only the shock
of the slap itself that had jarred Melissa into reality and pried off the entity's hold on her mind.
It had never occurred to me that the slap was due
to anything more than Melissa's uncontrolled fury.

I was still puzzled. Why would the spirit have wanted to harm Melissa in the first place? And why did Melissa feel the need to dominate the dead woman? What was the competition between them?

Sharma said the vile language only showed that Beth was existing on the lowest astral level, but Melissa, not knowing this, took it as a personal affront. She willfully and consciously attempted to dominate and silence Beth, who responded with the most powerful weapons she had: more obscenity and abuse. It seemed to Sharma that Beth's karma was probably related to some sexual aberration: We had learned, after all, that Beth had borne an illegitimate child; that she had had an illicit sexual relationship with Higgins at the time of the ship's sinking; and that she had, because of her lust for this man, allowed her daughter and her sister to perish in a fiery disaster. Her own desires had been—and still were—base and lurid. Here was Melissa, a beautiful and voluptuous woman, with the ability to perform the acts that Beth herself could perform only in fantasy and illusion. She would naturally feel intense jealousy and hatred, and wish, moreover, to possess this body, with which she would then have her way once more. Sharma thought quietly for a few moments.

"Melissa's emotional involvement may even have given Beth enough energy to throw that candle at her. It's obvious that the spirits you are contacting are using the energies you provide. Melissa, without realizing it, may have provided them with so much emotional energy that they were able not only to send messages, but also to perform physical acts."

"You mean that Melissa was, in a way, responsible for being hit by the ashtray?" I asked apprehensively.

"I'm not sure," said Sharma. "But I would think that's very close to the truth." Sharma sat for a few moments, looking thoughtfully at her plate. She hesitated, then looked directly at me.

"There's something else, Arnold," she said. "It occurs to me that the spirits may be preying on Melissa's vulnerability to get to you. I'm afraid it's you they want to destroy. They've tried it before." I turned away, unable to accept such a thought.

"Don't you see that you've entered a level of involvement that you really cannot control? You know the story and you've learned a great deal about the spirit world, and you've escaped with your sanity and your life. Can't you please stop now?"

I tried to control my irritation. I knew she meant well, and was speaking only out of concern for me, but it irked me that she continued to be so negative when it was exactly as she had said: close calls. As well as she knew me, she failed to see that I could control my emotions, remain detached. I had proved that to myself the night I had felt the presence in my bedroom. I told

Sharma about that experience, and although she looked at me steadily, she said nothing.

"Look, Sharma," I said, trying to console her. "I really have come to regard this whole business as an act of friendship. Zena appealed to us the very first night we contacted her. I didn't even believe they really were spirits. I'm still not absolutely sure what we're dealing with. But assuming it's all somehow real, the facts are that Zena's story has been consistent, and Beth and Higgins prove her accusations with every word they say. Why should Zena be made to suffer just because her sister has put her in this wretched position? It wasn't her fault that Beth had this child. She did more than her share as a sister and as a compassionate human being in taking the child as her own." The fact was, I did not fully understand how Zena had even become stuck in what Sharma called the astral realm. To me, she seemed as goodhearted a being as any living person I had known. She had asked nothing but for us to listen to her. Over and over again, she had told us the same story, asking us, imploring us to hear the truth. Why wasn't she already reincarnated? Why didn't her own goodwill take her to a higher place? And if there was something we could do for her, why should we not respond to her call for help?

Sharma thought before she spoke. "It is not an easy question," she said. She told me that at the moment a human being dies, the consciousness of that being is withdrawn from the physical plane and transferred to the astral. If the person is not yet very evolved, he clings fearfully to the security of his physical existence. The danger is that he becomes stuck in the astral plane where all existence is made of emotional illusions: pain, fear, lust, anger, hatred, a thousand yearnings unfulfilled. I had heard this explanation before, and began to grow impatient. But Sharma assured me that it was important for me to understand that it was the desire, *the longing for the physical world* that kept one fixed in the astral plane. Higher beings, she said—those who have lived many more lifetimes and are more evolved—pass easily through the astral as they ascend into the mental realm. Here, she said, physical and emotional matters are finally forgotten, but beings can become stuck here too, carried away by their own brain power, unable to conceive of any knowledge except the knowledge that comes from reason.

"As above, so below," said Sharma. "Those on earth who are intellectually oriented are most likely to be trapped by their own logic in the mental plane after death." The danger was, she told me, that they become satisfied with the existence there, which admittedly is very much sweeter than on the astral plane below. But there they remain until a light goes on, and they realize in an illuminating instant that this is not all there is to the universe. Once freed from the mental realm the soul can, after its next incarnation, sail through the astral and mental realms and into the spiritual plane. My head reeled as I tried to recall some of what I had read in my book on reincarnation.

"Can spirits on the mental plane ever contact us through the Ouija?" I wanted to know. "Are these the spirits that are responsible for phenomena like automatic writing?"

Sharma shook her head. "Psychic phenomena as most people experience them are astral. The energy is not of the mind, but of the emotions."

"What's enlightenment, then?"

"True enlightenment comes from higher regions —it's always electrifying, and always leaves the individual with knowledge he could not have gained through any other means. It's the ecstasy yogis and great teachers of the East try to prepare for all their lives. Few ever reach their goal." Sharma personally believed that true enlightenment was a matter of natural evolution—not only of each individual's karma, but of the entire system of life in the universe. And that very little, if anything, could be done to speed its coming.

"What happens to the spirit after it reaches the spiritual plane?" I thought I might as well pursue the questioning to its conclusion.

"What is said to happen is that the illumination we were talking about—the light that flashes at moments during the lifetimes of highly evolved people—becomes the whole existence of a soul on the spiritual level. They live what is called soul or cosmic consciousness, and all knowledge comes directly from The Source, unfiltered through physical needs, emotional feelings, or logic. It's the final step before ultimate spiritual freedom."

"It sounds as if a person is only some kind of a kernel—a spirit wrapped in layers of consciousness, the soul first, then mental, then emotional, and finally the physical shell."

"Well, not quite," Sharma said laughing. "The soul is not a wrapping for the spirit, it's a *joining* of the spirit to the physical. At conception the physical seed, fertilized, meets with a spirit waiting for reincarnation. This joining produces the soul."

"Once you've evolved into the spiritual state, do you still have to be reincarnated?" It seemed to me that living in a world of people jerked through life by their emotions or reasoning powers would be totally frustrating to anyone who no longer had need of such things.

"But the soul may still wish to express itself. In fact," Sharma said, "some might *choose* to come back—to act as lights for other people. Some poets, writers, and composers may have existed pretty much on the soul level of consciousness— their physical lives and needs did not seem to mean very much to them. The focus was elsewhere." She said eventually a person might not even need food or rest—but his total existence would take place on some different level which was very hard to understand.

"They walk in the light much of the time. All the spirit's past lives are imprinted on the shell of the soul—sort of like a memory bank—which at the final death cracks open and releases the spirit into the cosmic mass we call God."

I could feel my Episcopalian upbringing stirring—the image of God as a beneficent old man with a long beard. I knew this was simplistic and naive, but so firmly had it been ingrained that I couldn't hold a less personified concept in my head for very long.

"Wait a minute," I said. "If the spirit goes to God after the final death, where did it come from in the first place?"

"It came from God," she said. "Think of God as an enormous bonfire. The sparks that fly out are our spirits. They become coated with layers of physical, astral, and mental bodies, all of which must grow and learn. As these are shed one by one, the internal spark is released and flies back into the fire."

"But it's just a big circle," I protested. "Why go through it at all?" Sharma grinned.

"You might as well ask: Why the bonfire?"

I could not honestly say that I understood everything Sharma told me, and some of it I found just too ethereal to matter very much. How could anyone really know about any of this in the first place? After all, theories are nothing but logical patterns devised by people—unless: Could the knowledge actually be transmitted through someone in a state of soul consciousness? I wondered which of the poets or writers or composers, if any, actually lived in that state. I wondered if I ever could have met anyone who existed on this level—

since my reason told me there ought to be more highly evolved spirits today than in, say the sixteenth century. I wondered, if all this was true, what level I myself was existing on.

"The goal seems so remote," I said.

"But everyone gets there," said Sharma, "by his own rhythm—and through the help of inspiration of other people."

"Well then, can't we inspire Zena?" I asked.

"Impossible," said Sharma. "It's her karma to be where she is. Did it ever occur to you that Zena may have been a pompous and self-righteous person in life? Imagine taking in children not her own, accepting the responsibility, and probably making Beth feel very much ashamed and inferior. Maybe Zena was very holier-than-thou to Beth, and Beth resented her and hated her for it, even while she depended on her. I can think of many examples right now of just that relationship, can't you?"

I could—and it made me a little uncomfortable. Everyone, I imagined, who had siblings had similar feelings.

"When Zena understands where she is, and that all her existence is nothing more than an illusion, she'll be ready to move into her next incarnation. She may have to suffer on the astral plane many times more. There's no deadline, you know. And certainly *you* can't alter Zena's pattern. What makes you think you can?" I felt somewhat offended by Sharma's tone. I wasn't trying to become some kind of god. But I still wondered if our interaction with Zena couldn't help in some way.

"Consider this," I posed: "What if we believe her story, and tell others about it, and let her know that we do believe her. If we are able to free her from this illusion of guilt and entrapment, and from this terrible need to vindicate herself, maybe she'll be able to concentrate on her own development."

Sharma had no reply. "I just don't know," she said. "But it seems to me that Zena will probably be born many times and return many times to the astral plane before her problems work themselves out. Look at Beth. She's in even deeper trouble. She's not even trying to vindicate herself. She's still denying the facts in order to save her pride and protect herself."

What struck me as I mused about the whole situation was how very human it all was. How many people alive today live in worlds of illusion, seeming to ignore the facts, to pretend, to create a dreamworld to live in—and just for Beth's reasons: to protect themselves. It was as if the illusions of the death state were transported into the bodies of the living, or vice versa. The conclusion was overpowering: Death is nothing more than a continuation of life. If people in both dimensions could realize every minute exactly who and what and where they were, they would be spared a lot of illusionary pain. I suddenly saw Sharma's face before me, across the table. She was smiling.

"You've been deep in thought," she said. "Far away from me."

"You're right." I put my napkin down, reached across the table and took her hand. "But I'm here now," I told her.

NINTH ENCOUNTER

Friday, July 28

Two days later I drove out with the dogs in the new car. Joshua took to it right away and spent most of the trip asleep, but Rachel couldn't seem to get used to it. Finally, I took her onto the front seat, and after an hour or so of panting nervously out the window, she curled up and fell asleep with one blond ear draped over my knee.

The sun was obscured by dense clouds, and the sky seemed to grow lower and grayer the farther out I drove. "Oh no," I said, "not another storm."

On the ferry we were shrouded in fog, the low somber notes sounding often in the solitary night. Most of the passengers stayed below, but I went up on deck, not minding the dampness. Ever since my discussion with Sharma on Wednesday night, I had felt somehow more alive and more aware of my immediate surroundings, more conscious of my own being. It was an exhilarating sensation.

When I got to the house, the others were already there. François was with us again and full of stories about the previous weekend he had spent visiting friends on Block Island. His enthusiasm was a pleasure, and his stories were very amusing. François cooked again that evening—and we were full of genuine praise. Last weekend's fare, while good enough, could never measure up to François's cooking. He felt so up that he even tried to make a good show of remaining calm while we set about preparing the Ouija.

"You're not still playing that silly game?" he said. I glanced at him. Outwardly, he might have seemed devil-may-care, but I sensed the same old reflexive fear even through his heroic attempts to hide it. I thought of telling François what had happened the week before, to fill him in. But I thought better of it, and apparently so did everyone else. We all knew François very well—too well to assume he was actually blasé, when he had been so childishly fearful before. But we let well enough alone. Our feeling of camaraderie that evening might make a difference in his attitude. When we turned out the lights and sat down, François sat down, too. Howard volunteered to stay and write. He wouldn't have missed this session for anything, after what had happened last week. He was not about to believe that a candle flew across the room unless he saw it himself.

Once again, as soon as the three of us touched the upturned glass, the energy began. It was smooth, then hesitating, then smooth again. The glass moved rapidly around the letters, but the energy I felt was not the same as Zena's energy. Yet whenever Beth arrived there was a terrible, frustrating jerkiness—and tonight the movements of the glass were very smooth indeed. I was confused.

"What do you suppose it is?" I asked Michael.

"It feels different, doesn't it?" he said.

"Is that you, Zena?" I asked. I was not sure at all.

ZENA The glass repeated. ZENA HERE ZENA APPEARS

"What do you mean?"

THIS NIGHT ZENA CAN APPEAR YOU CAN SEE ZENA AND BETH ARNOLD MICHAEL FRANCOIS HOWARD YOU SEE TONIGHT

The four of us looked at one another. Michael looked around the room. François followed his gaze, but his eyes were full of fear.

"We don't see anyone, spirit," I said. "Where are you?"

NOT HERE INSIDE BEYOND DUNES

Howard read us the message.

"In the dunes?" he said. "They want us to meet them in the dunes?"

"It sounds that way," I said. Then, to the board: "You want us to go outside to the dunes? Where in the dunes?"

ALL GO OUTSIDE BOARDWALK TO WATER ISLAND

AT END OF BOARDWALK LOOK INTO DUNES YOU
WILL SEE BETH ZENA

"How can they do that?" I asked.

"They can't," said Howard.

"Maybe they can," said Michael. "God knows
they've done plenty of other things we couldn't
believe. I'd like to see what they look like." I was
skeptical. The idea that they would materialize
for us seemed unlikely, but if there was any possibility that they would, I certainly wanted to see it.

"Obviously, Zena wants to prove herself to us,"
said Michael. "She needs to assure us that she
actually exists. It makes perfect sense."

"You will be in the dunes, Zena?" I asked again.
The energy was strange, and I wanted to test the
spirit. "Are you Zena?"

YOU DOUBT ME ARNOLD COME COME TO DUNES
COME

We could read the message as it was given,
but waited for Howard to read it anyway.

ZENA IN BLUE DRESS BETH RED WE WAIT COME
NOW

There was no doubt. The instructions were
clear. Still we hesitated, not speaking. The glass
moved:

COME   And the energy stopped.

"Well, let's go," I said.

Outside it was foggy; the clouds had lowered
to the ground, making it impossible to see more
than a few feet ahead. François said he didn't
want to go out hunting for ghosts in the fog, and
I don't think there was a man among us who

could have faulted him for it. I didn't much feel like it either. But my curiosity drove me. Michael seemed to be all for the idea, but I doubted he would have gone alone.

"But it's the perfect time for them to materialize if they're going to," he said in a voice like a whisper. "The fog can act as a projection screen for them. Zena probably chose this night because conditions are just right."

Standing there on the deck, we could feel the penetrating dampness of the fog, and the chill of the night air. Howard and François went back inside for sweaters for us all.

"Well, I guess we'd better not keep the ladies waiting," said Michael, and started off down the stairs. We laughed nervously, very much on edge. The fog was so dense that we could not see where we were going. We walked single file along the narrow boardwalk, first Michael, then Howard, then François. I was last, and I fought to resist the temptation to keep looking back over my shoulder. We walked hesitatingly, touching the shoulder of the one ahead to keep together. It was a long walk to the end of the boardwalk, and making our way totally blind like this was not easy. We went silently, feeling each precarious inch with our feet—one false step and we could have dropped five feet into the beach briars that grew in the sand below.

Michael stopped suddenly in the darkness, and the rest of us stumbled, alarmed.

"What's that?" he whispered.

My heart was pounding. My hand was still on François's shoulder, and I could feel the tension in his body. He was scared to death.

"Listen," said Michael. We listened.

We heard the rhythmic crashing of the waves coming in, and then—from somewhere in the distance ahead of us—a low plaintive moaning. We stood frozen.

"What is that?" Howard asked.

"My God, let's go back," pleaded François.

"Wait a minute," I said. "Listen." We waited. Only the continuing roar of the ocean—nothing more. I told myself there was nothing to be afraid of. I remembered the night when I had been visited by an invisible intruder and had willed myself not to be afraid. The memory helped me detach myself. I braced François's shoulder reassuringly. "Don't worry. Let's go on."

We all walked on, still groping in the dark.

Suddenly Michael stopped again. "We're here," he said. "The end of the boardwalk." We all strained to see out into the dunes.

"Shall we go on a little farther?" Michael asked. He jumped down into the sand. The fog was so thick we couldn't see him.

"Where are you, Michael?" François called softly.

Michael lit a match and held it up to his face. "Here," he said. "Come on."

"Absolutely not," I said. "Don't be a fool—you'll get lost in the fog. We'll wait right here, as we were instructed." Michael climbed back up.

We waited about twenty minutes. Nothing happened. I didn't know whether I felt disappointed or relieved. It was cold and damp; there was no point in staying any longer.

"You see what I told you?" said Howard. "It's all absurd."

We threaded our way home along the boardwalk, growing more irritated because the way back was just as difficult as the way out—and nothing had been gained by our trip. By the time we reached the house, we were tired and soaked with fog, but more than anything we were very annoyed. Michael and I went straight to the table.

"I don't believe you guys," said Howard, peeling off his sweater. "How can you go on with this crazy thing?"

"Either this was a trick, or we were given wrong information," said Michael. I wasn't sure, but I knew I needed to find out what really was going on.

Immediately the energy was there, full force —that strange energy we had felt before. Howard and François were across the room, not wanting to be involved. I grabbed the yellow pad and pencil and wrote as best I could.

"What was the meaning of that?" I demanded of the glass, which sped smoothly around the letters.

YOU MUST GO AGAIN

"What do you mean?"

OTHER DIRECTION

"We were in the dunes, and you weren't there.

We will not go back. Who are you? Where is Zena?"

PLEASE GO AGAIN ZENA BLUE BETH RED BACK TOWARD PINES

"Pines?" Michael said to me. "We didn't go toward The Pines; we went toward Water Island. Those were the instructions, weren't they?" Howard came over, curious now, and took the yellow pad. He flipped through and found the spot. "Water Island." The glass moved.

WALK DOWN BOARDWALK TO PINES ONE HUNDRED YARDS WAIT ALL WILL APPEAR TONIGHT

The energy ceased. I called for Zena, wanting to ask more questions. But the energy simply was not there.

"What should we do?" I asked Michael.

"Are you nuts?" Howard said. "You're certainly not going back out."

"Come on, Howard," said Michael. "The worst that can happen is we won't see anything. But what if they're really there? Maybe they tried to materialize, and they couldn't. Maybe the conditions weren't right. Maybe they got their directions mixed up." Given the unreasonable situation, it seemed reasonable to me. I was willing to make another attempt to see them. Michael went into his room to get his windbreaker to protect him against the dampness. I pulled on a jacket.

Since Michael and I were determined, Howard decided he would come along, too, although he made it plain he did not expect to see anything.

François echoed Howard's sentiments, but the truth was that he was far too frightened to stay alone in the house. He came.

We walked out into the fog again, this time in the opposite direction. We followed the boardwalk, hand to shoulder, for about a hundred yards, then stopped and peered all around us. We could see a few lights in the houses among the dunes, all shrouded in fog.

"What's that?" said François. "Is that something?" We all looked. Fog. We kept looking, waiting. "Wait," said François again. "I'm sure I see something now. Two forms, there, in the dunes." We strained our eyes to see, but could make out nothing less amorphous than rolls of fog drifting among the dunes. François insisted.

"François, there's nothing there," Howard said. Michael and Howard stepped to the edge of the boardwalk to relieve themselves. The air was raw and chilly, and we were very uncomfortable. We waited there for about twenty minutes, but we saw nothing.

"All right," I said. "Let's get out of here."

This time we all went to the table and the glass. There was no need for a question; the glass moved instantly.

YOU SEE I DO HAVE YOU IN MY CONTROL I CAN MAKE YOU DO WHAT I WANT DO NOT INTERFERE

I got up from the table and snapped on the light, unwilling to go on.

"Wait a minute, Arny," Michael said. "Don't you want to . . . ?"

"This whole evening has been wasted," I said. "We can't figure out if we're dealing with Zena or Beth or Higgins or some other depraved soul, and we are allowing ourselves to be controlled. That's enough for one night. Let's have some music—play some cards." I was annoyed with myself for having allowed myself to be taken in.

"I'm glad to see you've come to your senses," said Howard, getting out the cards. Howard shuffled. "Five-card, fifty cents and a dollar," he said. "Low man opens."

We cleared the big coffee table and played there. I drew some good cards, but I couldn't keep my mind on the game.

"It really gets me that Beth tricked us," I said.

"But the energy wasn't like Beth's," said Michael.

"Are you two going to play or talk?" said Howard. I considered my hand and threw in another two quarters.

"You forget that we have never spoken to Beth without the presence of another spirit," I said. "Zena always is there trying to get control away from her."

"Actually, it's the other way around, isn't it?" Michael corrected.

"Yes—but nevertheless, that's what created the struggle on the board, and that halting energy flow. On the other hand, when Higgins is with her, the energy is electrifying." I remembered those sessions, when the power I felt though my body was intoxicating. I wondered why, if the spirits actually did siphon energy from us, the energy we felt was different for each of them.

François was gathering a pile of coins toward his side of the table. It was my deal. "Same game," I said, shuffling. "So you think that somehow Beth was able to lock Zena away and control the board herself? How could Zena have allowed that? Why didn't she come and warn us? Zena has always been able to control Beth. Where was Zena?"

"Remember they told us that Zena would not be coming back again," Michael said.

"I wonder what they did to her," I said. "Do you think we'll never be able to reach her again?"

"Good riddance," said François, raising the bet by half a dollar. We all saw his bet, and Michael won the pot with a full house over François's three queens.

I didn't want to think that we never would be able to contact Zena again. She was the only one with any information, any logical message to give us. I cared about her.

"You open, Arny," said Howard. Then I realized what I had been doing, and laughed. We all laughed. "I'll open with one buck," I said. We played until two in the morning. I lost eight dollars.

TENTH ENCOUNTER

Saturday, July 29

The next morning the fog lingered densely until about nine, then gradually burned off. By noon the day was crystal clear, the sky was cornflower blue. I walked out on the beach with the dogs, sipping coffee. There were people on the beach, under umbrellas, on towels, in the surf. Somewhere, a radio blared rock. Suddenly it seemed vaguely obscene to me, all those bodies baking in the sun like so much meat, although I had done it myself many times before, and would doubtless join them that very afternoon. I thought of the night before, and all that fog; all of us feeling our way in the darkness, fingers to shoulders through the mist, looking for ghosts in the dunes. Had we actually done that? Had that happened? My life was taking on the quality of a dream, and that morning I still was not awake.

As I walked back up the beach to take my cup to the house, a man emerged from Max's house and walked over to me. It was Joey, a painter friend who was staying with Annie and Max for the weekend. Joey had been dispatched to ask if I would come over at ten o'clock that evening to help them with a favor. They were having a dinner party, and wanted me to take a photograph of them at the table.

"Of course," I said. "I'll be happy to." I spent the rest of the day on the beach, as planned. I found myself being drawn into conversations with friends and neighbors. Michael and a friend of his—another sculptor—were building in the moist sand near the water's edge. I was so interested that I went along to see how it would turn out, and the result was that the three of us, later joined by five or six children, constructed a sand castle at least as long as an average-size room. It was the most intricate structure imaginable, and several passersby took pictures of it.

Toward evening I felt very much refreshed, the world of people and the world of spirits much more in proportion—or at least the proportions I had always assigned them. Finally, a normal day. I stood under a cool shower for a long time, enjoying the sharpness of the spray, then dressed and took a book to the living room. Gradually the others drifted in from the beach or wherever they had been all afternoon. Nobody seemed very anxious to do anything.

Eventually, someone asked François when dinner was going to be ready. He became incensed. He informed us haughtily that he was not the cook, and that we should not assume that he was going to do all the cooking just because he was there. Howard, who could barely boil an egg, looked up from his book.

"All right, François," he said. "I see your point. I'll cook tonight."

Howard went into the kitchen, and soon there were sounds of the refrigerator door and cupboard drawers opening and closing—all to the accompaniment of casual whistling. I smiled to myself, but was careful not to look up from my book. At last François could stand it no longer. He drifted over to the kitchen and struck up a conversation with Howard, asking what he was preparing, and offering suggestions about how to go about it. Within ten minutes Howard was back on the sofa stirring a new martini with his index finger.

I looked at my watch. Nearly ten.

"I'm going to play photographer for a few minutes," I announced. I crossed to the kitchen and sniffed. "Whatever it is you're cooking in there, Howard, it sure smells good." François turned from the sink and narrowed his eyes. "See you later," I said.

I walked out onto the deck and down the wooden steps to the walk that joined the two houses. I could hear sounds of conversation coming from Max's deck, so I walked around to the front of the house and up onto the deck. The dinner table had been set up outside. Colored banners fluttered

down from the roof overhang. The table was set
for four, with a huge clam shell filled with flowers
for the centerpiece. Plain, natural-colored crock-
ery plates sat on rush mats, with scallop shells for
salad. Glasses for wine and water stood at each
place, sparkling in the light of candles under glass
hurricane chimneys, and silvery-looking coolers
at each end of the table held bottles of white wine
chilling in ice. Max stood with his back to the
ocean and focused his Polaroid on the table. Then
he asked me to stand in the same spot while he
sat down with Annie, Joey, and another friend.
Everyone was in a gay party mood, and there was
a great deal of laughter as I pretended to be
completely at a loss with the ridiculously simple
camera. I snapped the picture and took the camera over to Max, who pulled out extraneous scraps
of paper to be discarded. Sixty seconds later, the
picture was ready.

It was a good, clear shot; the color was excellent. "But what's that?" I asked. Above the table
in the picture were the cloudlike but definitely
recognizable shapes of two women. My stomach
did an involuntary somersault. We all gaped at
the picture in Max's hand. The ghostlike forms
were rosy-bluish in color, bluer around the outlines, rosier toward the centers. They had no faces,
but there was no mistaking the outlines of their
hair, their arms, their long dresses. I could do
nothing but stare. The others looked at me, then
at the air above the table, then at me. I snatched

the picture and rushed back home to show the others.

"Hey, wait a minute!" Max shouted after me. "What is that? Where are you going?"

François was beside himself when he saw it: At first he insisted they looked exactly as he had thought—he swore he had seen just these same two forms out in the dunes the night before. We ignored him. Howard examined the picture closely, turning it at every angle to the light. But he could not explain it in any way. He used words like "superimposition" and "halation," but nothing made rational sense, and he knew it.

A few years later, a nature photographer would discover such halations in more scientific settings: He would photograph a leaf growing on a branch, then pluck off the leaf and click the shutter again, to capture not the leaf but a kind of energy field in the shape of the leaf. But he would be using a special camera with special film. I was using a Polaroid. The picture was a complete mystery.

We had our own dinner very late, and decided, much to François's relief, that it would be best to leave the Ouija alone tonight. Michael and I, at least, needed to prove to ourselves that we were not under its control. It was a strange victory to walk away from the table, away from the house, and down to the discotheque.

At a party during the week, Sharma and I met a professional actor named Gerald O'Connor, whose avocation was astrology. Sharma, of course, had been raised on astrology, but I had only the layman's curiosity. I had lots of questions, though, and Gerald invited me to have my own chart done. I wasn't sure I wanted to go that far, but Sharma encouraged me. So I told him what he wanted to know: my date, time, and place of birth. We made a date for Thursday evening for my reading.

Thursday evening I arrived at O'Connor's apartment and was shown to a table with a place marked for me by a pad of lined paper and a pencil. Across the table sat the astrologer, with a circular chart and several pages of typewritten notes. He proceeded to tell me what my life had been like up to then, and what it was going to be like in the future. Some of it was surprisingly accurate—disturbingly so, in fact—and much sounded to me like wild speculation. But a great deal of it consisted of specific events that were to occur on fairly specific dates. Sharma had been right—it was very interesting. I took reams of notes, and went home that evening to transfer the important prophecies to my calendar, so I could see if they actually would occur.

By midnight the project was only half finished, so I decided to continue in bed. I stacked pillows, set the alarm clock for seven thirty, and settled down to continue my transcription. An hour later I was bleary-eyed and unable to stay awake any longer. I folded the notes inside the calendar, put it on my bedside table with my red pencil on top, checked to see that the alarm clock was cocked, and turned off the light.

The next time I opened my eyes, it was broad daylight. I looked to see what time it was. The clock wasn't there. I was seized by the panicky feeling that afflicts those who oversleep on the day of an important business appointment. I leaped out of bed and grabbed my watch, which was on the dresser. Eight fifteen. I ran into the shower and stood under the rushing spray, my mind traveling over the evening before. How strange that the clock had not rung. But how could it have rung? It wasn't even there.

Not there! I stepped out of the shower, not bothering to turn off the faucets. I grabbed a towel and ran into the bedroom to look. There was the table, the lamp, the red pencil. No clock, no calendar, no horoscope notes. I looked to see if they had fallen on the floor. They had not. I got down on my hands and knees and searched under the bed and the chair. Nothing.

I was baffled, but there was no time now. I went back and turned off the water, shaved, and dressed. My appointment was at nine o'clock uptown. If I skipped breakfast and grabbed a taxi, I could make it. What I really wanted to do was to look for my clock and my calendar. To hell with the meeting, I said. They'll just have to wait. I searched everywhere, beginning with the immediate area of the table. I scoured the place, looked under the furniture, in the fireplace, even in the trash. I found my alarm clock under the sofa. It was set, but the alarm trigger had been pushed in. I rushed outside to search the garbage cans before they were emptied: three cans, their lids chained to the fence. I found whiskey bottles, bent cans, package wrappings, Kleenex, fruit rinds. No calendar or papers of any kind.

Later that day, as Sharma and I were driving out to Fire Island with our three dogs wrestling in the back seat, I told her about the strange event. She connected everything to my business with the spirits, becoming surprisingly agitated. She said they were a part of my life now, and she could think of no way to get rid of them.

"Stop it now," she pleaded. "Protect yourself. Never have anything to do with the spirit world again. If you're lucky, they'll drift away from you of their own accord." She really was very concerned.

"Look Sharma," I said testily. "Who knows how those papers disappeared, or how the alarm clock got under the sofa? Maybe I sleepwalked and did it all myself. Maybe the apartment was broken into during the night."

"Was anything else disturbed?" she asked.

"No, only that."

"Thieves usually do not engage in games of hide-and-seek," she said.

"Sharma, I can't stop now, and that's the way it is. Now let's talk about something else." Sharma felt a little hurt, and I felt badly for having spoken so sharply to her. "Well, I may as well tell you what else happened, since you'll learn it anyway as soon as we arrive." I told her about the preceding weekend, the ghost hunt through the fog in the dunes, the shocking photograph with the bluish-pink, cloudlike figures suspended in air. Sharma looked at me pleadingly. I had the feeling it wasn't the search, nor the spirits' promise of materialization that surprised her, nor the fact that they had appeared on film—but that in spite of all these events, I should continue to be so stubborn.

"Where is the picture?" she wanted to know.

"It's at Max's place. You can see it as soon as we get there."

Joey and his friend had left during the week, but both Annie and Max were at home, and they were delighted to show the photo to Sharma. "We all know that you've been doing something behind closed doors, because no one ever sees you socially at night; but why would ghosts appear at our house?" Max asked. "And if there really are spirits, how can they be photographed? I don't understand any of this." Reluctantly, I explained the whole story to them. It wasn't a good idea, I knew, to extend the population of those who were privy to our strange proceedings. We weren't even sure of them ourselves. But Max and Annie had been accidentally involved, and there was nothing I could do.

Sharma took the picture, looked at it, and handed it back, inscrutable as always—and I suppose still a little hesitant about speaking after our episode in the car.

"Well?" said Annie. "What do you think? Do you believe it?"

"I'm sure it's the two spirits," Sharma said.

"But how can you photograph ghosts?" Annie asked.

"It's the etheric body," Sharma said with hesitation in her voice. I knew she really didn't want to get into this, but I encouraged her anyway.

"What is that?" I asked.

"The etheric is the energy of every living thing," she said without enthusiasm. "After the spirit leaves the physical body at death, there remains the etheric body—an exact replica of the physical."

"Is that the spirit?" Annie encouraged her.

"No, it's something different," Sharma said. "It's like a zone of energy incorporated into our bodies. Clairvoyants claim to see it around living people and to be able to tell if a person is sick, and sometimes which parts of the body are afflicted, by looking at the radiations of the etheric body."

I still didn't understand. This etheric body was something we hadn't talked about before, and I wanted to know how it related to the astral, mental, and all those other bodies. If everything Sharma said was true, life and death were extremely complicated.

"Our physical bodies are patterned after our etheric ones," Sharma said.

"Shouldn't it be the other way around?"

"No. The physical body is the most temporary."

Max and Annie listened with great fascination. They did not actually know the events that had taken place at our house every weekend. The photograph had suddenly aroused their interest.

I still was not satisfied with the explanation. Why didn't the etheric body disintegrate after death? What held it together when the physical body was gone?

"When a person isn't very evolved—a young soul," Sharma said, "his etheric body can linger for a very long time near the place of death. The pull of the soul is too weak to overcome the person's strong physical attraction to material things. The etheric body cannot adjust to the new state of detachment. It wants to remain near the earthly environment, near its earthly body."

Sharma told us that a highly evolved being would leave his etheric body practically at the moment of death, since he would not be interested in clinging to the physical earth. The etheric body would disintegrate, and at the next incarnation the spirit would have a new one.

"Well then, why, if it disintegrates, haven't Zena's and Beth's?" I asked. Her eyes looked steadily at me, and her passiveness changed to an expression of earnest concern.

"They are clinging to the earth," she said evenly. "They are bound by their desire for physical existence. They want to attack and possess in order to fulfill their desires."

I felt a twinge of nervousness in my stomach. "And what happens when they attack?" I wanted to know.

"When the entity attacks, its body coexists along with your own, separately but together. Sometimes the possessed person can see them himself: faces and horrible masks that appear at night just before he drifts off to sleep. Or one might hear them as voices in one's head, strange voices, sometimes wordless, curiously pitched. Or their presence might be sensed in drained energy, lack of concentration." Sharma said her teacher had told her that in saloons he watched drunks slumped over the bar, possessed by alien beings, entities who forced the alcoholics to keep drinking, to feed the entities' own insatiable needs.

"It is very important that you stop the séances, Arnold," she said. "You are taking an awful chance —you're inviting possession." I wished she hadn't said that, not here, not in front of Max and Annie. I felt embarrassed, and she sensed that she had overstepped her bounds. "It's an interesting thing," she said lightly, in a voice that changed the topic and the mood, "this Western tradition of mourning the departed at death."

"Why is that interesting?" asked Annie. "When someone you love very much dies, it is natural to be sad. You don't have them anymore."

"And that person has lost his life," Max added. "A human life."

"He only has lost his physical life," Sharma said. "Actually, he has entered another existence."

"If you believe in that sort of thing," said Max.

"When people mourn, it's really very selfish," Sharma said. "It's all negative energy, sentimentality that appeals to the spirit's emotions and holds him to the earth. The spirit suffers because he's held when he longs to be released."

"But we're mourning because we're feeling sorry for ourselves," said Annie. "Why should our emotions have any effect on the dead?"

"Because the soul still is very human, still responds to human sentiments. People on the other side are still people. Death is not so special, you know. It's just another step in life—a series of lives. The best and quickest way to speed the spirit on its way is to cremate the body in twenty-four hours and then ignore it altogether."

"Why twenty-four hours?" Max asked.

"It generally takes that long for the spirit to disengage itself from the physical remains," Sharma replied. "But the main thing is to get rid of the coffins, the flowers, the rituals of death. None of it is spiritual; it's all emotional. And it's not done for the dead, but for the living—and is detrimental to both."

"What about Zena and Beth?" I asked. "They died, presumably without burial, without funeral, certainly without flowers. What are they still doing here?"

"They're here because of their own weaknesses, not anyone else's," Sharma said, becoming impatient with me. "Your game is not helping. You have given them a key to get back into the physical world. The séances might even be prolonging their stay in the astral world."

This was something I had not thought of. I had been harboring the hope that, if what Sharma said was true about the ethereal realms and reincarnation, our contact with the spirits would not only yield us information, but would actually be beneficial to Zena. Deep inside, I wanted to be able to say that I had freed an earthbound spirit. Sharma knew it, and that was why she kept telling me it was impossible.

"Don't play God," she said, after we had said good-bye to Annie and Max. "You are not equipped to do anything but prolong their misery and endanger your own life. And your own evolutionary progress." She sighed. "But I suppose that's your karma. I'm sorry, Arnold. It's just that I care for you so much."

Sharma and I walked back to our own deck. The sun was low in the west, its rays turning the sand to gold and the ocean to deep turquoise. The last of the sunbathers had straggled back to their houses to get ready for the evening, leaving the beach void and desolate. Only the ocean was alive, unspeakably beautiful.

"Don't worry, Arnold," Sharma said, touching my arm. "They'll be released eventually. They can stay where they are for a thousand years. Years are earthtime. To them, time has no relevance. A thousand years is like an instant, or an instant like a thousand years.

"The two sisters fought a battle when they were

alive. Love, protection, resentment, jealousy. They're still fighting. One to tell the story, one to deny it. Eventually, they'll realize that what happened in their past life is no longer meaningful —that they don't have to cling to it anymore."

I walked over to the railing at the edge of the deck. The real was becoming confounded with the unreal again. What were the facts? I tried to sort things out. The Ouija lost on every count. It was frightening for François, unimportant to Howard, dangerous for Melissa, who was nonetheless drawn to it, a heartache for Sharma, whom I cared for very much, and a threat to me. Because of spirits I had nearly lost my life twice. Sharma insisted that they already had become a part of my life. And furthermore, I was not even doing what I wanted so much to do—help Zena. Zena had not appeared at our last session, and during the previous session she had been overwhelmed by Beth and Higgins. I felt terrible about that, as if I had let a friend down. And then, added to the struggle I felt about the Ouija itself, there was the greater question: Maybe Sharma was wrong. Maybe all this actually did have some other logical explanation, and we were elaborating too much.

I was having trouble thinking about it. I looked at Sharma, who was gazing out to sea. I had disturbed even her serenity; seldom did she show her feelings as she had tonight.

Yet none of these facts, however strong, could deter me. I had to find Zena again.

ELEVENTH ENCOUNTER

Friday, August 4

Just about sunset, people began arriving at our house, dressed for a cocktail party we had been invited to at Geoffrey Lloyd's. Geoffrey was a well-known literary agent who had a small house a few boardwalks away in the center of the Island. Sharma had put on a white linen pantsuit with a deep décolletage. She looked sensational, the white linen setting off tanned olive skin and shiny, raven hair in waves over her shoulders. Melissa came looking fabulous, too, wearing a diaphanous, peach-colored caftan. François and Michael had arrived by ferry not long before; Howard had come out to the house early, but had gone on ahead to the party with some other friends.

When we arrived, the party was in full swing with rock music and a tended bar, and people so packed into the little house that they spilled out onto the deck. The big house in front of Geoffrey's had been washed away by the hurricane of 1960, leaving its smaller neighbor with a beautiful ocean-front view. Geoffrey came out for only part of the summer, and rented the place out for the rest of the season. In fact, this was the house where Chita Rivera had been staying the summer before when she had rescued me from drowning. I didn't know Chita then; I had first met her the time when I was half dead on the beach. But the following winter, on a beach in Puerto Rico walking with Sharma, I heard a voice call out behind me, "Please don't go in the water!" I turned to see Chita's laughing face, and marveled that she had recognized me.

At the party, our little company dissolved into the throng as we spotted familiar faces among the guests. There were many theater and literary people—actors, actresses, playwrights, authors—and pretty boys from the beach. Geoffrey found Sharma and me immediately. He grabbed a drink from a passing tray and pressed it into Sharma's hands, at the same time introducing me to the immediate circle as the local warlock—word had apparently gotten around. He meant it as a lighthearted joke, but a fascinated little group gathered around and began asking questions. I was in no mood to get myself involved in any serious conversations just then, and I tried to make light of the whole situation, much to Sharma's relief. But if our Ouija was not allowed to become the topic of the evening, it nevertheless found its way into small private talks throughout the party. I heard Melissa talking about it enthusiastically to three or four people whose faces were unfamiliar to me. She was very animated, their expressions rapt.

But even our spirits were upstaged by talk of an extravaganza that had recently taken place at a large house up the beach from us. It was a "Fellini party"—all the guests had to come in Felliniesque costumes, which meant very imaginative, rather decadent, and not a little grotesque. One girl was made up as a pure-black rooster, with black tights and huge black tail feathers, her hair slicked back like a helmet under a blood-red cock's-comb headdress. The bodice of her skintight body suit had been cut in curves that circled below her breasts; her nipples had been painted black. Another girl came as a black widow spider—her costume consisted exclusively of fine, black webbing representing a spiderweb draped from her shoulders to the floor; beneath the web she was totally nude. One man, less erotically inclined, had fastened himself to a clutch of huge helium-filled balloons and hopped joyfully about. Another man had stolen the show: He was in drag—a black leather nail-studded jacket over a black satin maillot-style swimsuit and mesh opera hose with high-heeled shoes. His face was dramatically made up like a woman's, but on his head he wore a motorcycle helmet.

The house itself was one of those fabulous multilevel cantilevered ones, with weathered siding and miles of glass facing the sea. The deck had been beautifully planted, and for the occasion a champagne fountain had been installed. It was the spectacle of the year, except for one element that really was too decadent: among the champagne fountains and buffet tables full of delicacies, there also were bowls of pills, marijuana, and hash—just about any drug you wanted to indulge in.

Sharma and I came home from Geoffrey's party at around nine thirty; the others straggled in later.

Dinner was one of Sharma's masterpieces: a seafood curry. She made a kind of yellow bean called dhal, and a salad of cucumbers in yogurt. There was more wine, of course, and even François and Michael, who rarely drank anything, were merrily quaffing Pouilly-Fuissé with the rest of us. By the time we got around to thinking about Beth and Zena, it was very late, and we were feeling extremely relaxed.

Michael set up the board while Sharma and I took care of cleaning up the kitchen. The others made no move to help, but continued laughing and talking. Michael had to work around them. The party atmosphere was so strong that I found myself wondering if we could actually make contact with the spirits tonight.

Sharma was very gay on the surface, but she ventured to mention to me once, in a casual way, that I ought to take care for François and Melissa —and perhaps Michael as well—who, because they had been drinking, might be particularly easy prey for the spirits. She had told me before that people who are under the influence of alcohol should never tamper with anything supernatural, for the alcohol weakens their constitutions and makes them vulnerable. She did not press the point, but I assured her that I would help her keep an eye on Melissa and the two men, and be ready to stop the session just in case. It would have been easy enough to call the whole session off right then; nobody would have objected very strenuously. But I was determined to contact Zena. It had been too long since we had been able to reach her.

I set the mood by turning off all the lights in the living room, ritualistically, one by one. I lit the candle and placed it on the table, moving slowly, not speaking. Melissa was chattering amiably. I held her eyes for a moment with mine, and she stopped talking. Quickly the room became silent. We took our places. Michael, Melissa, and I were working the Ouija that evening. François watched, not wanting to leave. The times he had left he had missed something.

Howard was in no condition to take notes, so Sharma volunteered. In fact, Howard excused himself at the last minute and announced he was going out. Good for Howard, I thought. He knows himself very well. I couldn't help drawing a contrast with François, who hung around against his better judgment.

We turned out the light from the huge iron chandelier above us and began. Nothing happened.

"Zena, we are here," I said. "We wish to talk to Zena." After a few seconds the energy was smooth and regular, the familiar flow of Zena's presence.

YES MY FRIENDS YOU HAVE COME BACK

"Zena, is that you?"

ZENA SO LONG LONELY IN SEA

"Are you all right? Where did they take you? What happened?"

NEVER ALLOW BETH SHE HIGGINS EVIL THEY CAN DESTROY THEY CAN POSSESS

"But what did they do to you last week?" I persisted. "Where were you?"

DEEP IN SEA ZENA STRONG BETH AND HIGGINS TOO STRONG FOR ZENA TOGETHER TOO STRONG LONELY GRAVE ALL ALONE

"Are you alone now?" I asked. "Is Beth here with you?"

YES NO DO NOT ALLOW BETH I WILL PROTECT

"How can we help you, Zena? We want to help."

MELISSA STRONG DO NOT ALLOW BETH DANGER TO ALLOW BETH CAN POSSESS

"We understand Beth is evil. Zena, how can we help you?"

I HELP YOU

"What do you mean?"

FRIENDS NEW FRIENDS I PROTECT YOU DO NOT FEAR

"What is there to fear? Is Beth here?"

NO YES SHE IS NEARBY I CONTROL HER PLEASE TELL MY STORY RED NIGHT COLD COLD NIGHT ALL DEAD CHILD NOT MINE NOT MINE

There was a sudden jerk on the board, and the glass spun wildly, haltingly, not touching any of the letters. We could feel the fearsome presence of the evil sister. I struggled to control the board.

"Leave us, Beth," I commanded in a firm voice. "We want only to talk to Zena."

WAIT TEN

A struggle, then the energy left us abruptly as it had in earlier sessions. We waited quietly, watchfully, wondering if it would return. I kept my finger poised lightly on the glass. In a few minutes, the smooth energy of Zena returned, and the glass raced confidently again, circling, waiting.

"Tell us what you want us to know," I said.

MY STORY TELL MY STORY INNOCENT CHILD NOT MINE DEAD BECAUSE OF BETH WEEP FOR ROSA-MOND CHILD OF FEAR

"Yes, Zena, we know about Rosamond. We know she was not your child. We know Beth is . . ." The glass tore itself out of our reach and there was a fearful antagonism on the board again as Beth's presence interfered with Zena's. The energy was halting and maddeningly hesitant. I tried again to summon Zena. But before I could utter a word, I was seized by a terrific bolt of energy, like a sudden jolting electric shock pulsing through my body. I felt myself jerk reflexively. It was almost impossible to keep up with the glass as it raced from letter to letter.

HIGGINS WILL DESTROY ALL DO NOT INTERFERE

"That bastard," said Melissa testily. Sharma shot her a glance, then looked up at me. Michael remained passive, engrossed in the proceedings.

MELISSA HERE FILTHY BITCH MELISSA FEARS WEAK

"I won't listen to you," said Melissa fiercely. "Zena, where are you?"

ZENA NO MORE

"We wish only to speak to Zena," I said.

ZENA NO MORE ARNOLD NO MORE ARNOLD WILL DIE

"We won't speak to you, Beth," I insisted. "Only Zena."

I ZENA ARNOLD GO OUTSIDE WALK TEN PACES INTO OCEAN THERE YOU WILL SEE ZENA

"No way, Beth," I said. "Now where is Zena?"

ARNOLD I WILL DESTROY

"Your threats can't hurt us," Melissa shouted. "You can't hurt us."

BETH POWER GREAT MELISSA CUNT FUCKING CUNT

"*La putaine,*" raged François, his eyes full of fury. Sharma put her hand on his arm, and he settled back. Melissa was drawn deeper and deeper into the Ouija. She could not control herself. The spirits continued to call Melissa and François filthy names, and even Sharma bore the brunt of many of the insults. I kept calling for Zena, trying to keep the others from involving themselves further. But it was to no avail; their emotional involvement only gave more power to the fury of the fearsome hate of Beth and Higgins. Theirs was a world of guilt and hatred—two emotions that cannot exist without others to feed it. And there was plenty of nourishment for them at that table. I was sick of it.

"Shut up, all of you!" I shouted above their voices. There was silence. The glass kept speeding, but we ignored its messages. "You're helping them," I pleaded with François and Melissa. "They are feeding on your emotional display. Don't you see how you encourage them? Beth is disgusting. Don't let her control this meeting. We want to be in control." The amazingly strong current of energy continued.

HIGGINS CONTROLS HIGGINS CONTROLS HIGGINS WILL DESTROY ALL

No matter what I said, no matter how many times I invoked Zena, we could never reach her for more than a plaintive word or two. The energy patterns through my body as each spirit took control were shocking and debilitating. I could feel myself weakening, and there was nothing I could do. I fought to remain detached, and fill myself with strength. But the effort itself was draining. If only we could see the spirits and know what they were doing to Zena. We got nothing but insults and threats, and horrible language. Melissa and François couldn't think of vile enough retorts, so incomprehensibly intent were they on winning this verbal battle. I couldn't understand it, and I was utterly helpless.

Suddenly the light went on full force, and we jumped back from the table. Sharma was standing beside the light switch.

"That's enough," she said.

TWELFTH ENCOUNTER

Saturday, August 5

There just didn't seem to be any point to it anymore. The séances were going nowhere. What
had begun at the start of the summer as an exciting adventure, a fascinating experiment, had
degenerated into a battleground of frustration,
fear, and anger. I really had been too hard on
François, I realized then. And I never should
have allowed Melissa in on the sessions; because
of her, three of them had had to be cut short.
Too many people had become involved, fueling
spirits with energy and agitating people to heightened emotional states that bordered on frenzy.

I decided to take my English friends up on
their invitation. The only way I could get away
from the strain and anxiety of this strange summer was to force myself to leave. Quickly I called
a travel agent and booked reservations. That

done, I felt relieved and curiously eager to start afresh with the Ouija knowing that for myself, at least, there were now only a few chances left before I would go away.

Maybe we ought to continue the séances without any outsiders, I thought as Sharma and I were walking up the beach toward Water Island.

Robert Chambers, who had wrapped up his shooting on the coast and had come east to promote his film, was staying with Hank and Melissa for the weekend (Hank and he were old school chums). We had been invited to join them for lunch. Sharma and I had met Bob a couple of times in town; it would be good to see him again and catch up on the world of Hollywood.

It was hot that day. Really hot. The sky was cloudless, and impossible to look at in the intense glare of the sun. Sharma and I carried our sandals as we waded along the edge of the water; we had needed them to walk on the dry, scorching sand. There wasn't a whisper of a breeze to relieve the heat. I looked out to the cool, rolling water, longing to race into the waves and just float in the coolness. But I couldn't do it. The influence of the Ouija had been too strong. If anyone had asked why I had not gone into the water above my waist all summer, I would not have told the truth—because the truth was that I was afraid. I was a good swimmer, but the ocean was no longer my ally. I bent down to scoop some water onto my arms and shoulders to cool them. A young boy with a slab of wood ran along the shallow water, threw the slab onto the slick surface, jumped on with both feet, and rode the board a good twenty feet. I smiled. Riding the surface of an ocean that contained dangers beyond his imagination. It was his innocence that protected him, I thought. No, even innocence could not protect one against certain things. I had been innocent once, and had nearly been drowned by a force I hadn't imagined either.

"When Michael and I worked the Ouija by ourselves," I said to Sharma, "it seemed to progress beautifully. Just enough energy to contact Zena, all the concentration we needed, with no extraneous lack of self-control." Sharma made no reply. "Maybe that's the answer," I repeated, thinking out loud. "His intuitive plugging into the power, my detached approach to the whole thing. We get information, we avoid conflict. And we don't have to contend with François or Melissa or any others who can't keep themselves in check."

"It won't work," Sharma said simply. "It's gone too far."

"Maybe so," I replied, not wishing to launch an argument. "But there's only one way to find out."

When we arrived at Hank's place, we were totally parched. Melissa rescued us with tall glasses of fresh iced tea with mint leaves from their herb garden.

Bob looked terrific. He had a California tan and was in fine form, the movie having gone well for him. It is rare that television actors, even very good ones with tremendous followings, can cross over into motion pictures. But Bob had made the transition successfully. The film was completed and soon to be released. He had brought with him his latest conquest, a young English-woman named Diane who worked as a costume mistress on the film. She was a sexy-looking woman with long, shining, chestnut hair and green eyes. She reminded me of a young Elizabeth Taylor. Diane was the first to bring up the subject of Zena and Beth. Melissa evidently had been telling her about it, and she was eager to hear more. It turned out that she herself was very much involved with the world of extrasensory perception and psychic energies. Her mother and her grandmother both were well-known claivoyants in England. They had belonged to the Theosophical Society, an organization of people who had an intellectual approach to God and religion and believed in reincarnation. Diane herself had had experiences with séances and with the Ouija, and she was fascinated that we had been able to sustain contact with what appeared to be the same spirits week after week. She had respect for the power of the spirits that made such contact possible.

"I have seen people possessed," she told us. "It isn't a pretty sight."

Bob apparently had no idea that his girl was attached so closely to the supernatural.

"Come on, Diane," he said, "that's hokey."

"Well, I have to admit that most mediums are

phonies," she said, "but there are a few genuine ones who can reach the dead. But only for a very short time after death." I had heard this before: that spirits could be contacted only during a few days after their deaths. "It takes a few days for the etheric body to dissolve and free the spirit," Diane continued. "If you try to reach them after that, they simply aren't there. They've gone to the next plane of development."

At the term "etheric body," I glanced at Sharma, who appeared interested but aloof. So far, she had been our only source for this kind of information, and I suppose she was glad to have her facts verified. But then a very big question arose in my mind. If spirits of the departed could only be reached within a few days after death, how could we be contacting the spirits of people who died a hundred years ago?

"They just couldn't bring themselves to leave the earth," Diane said.

"Earthbound," I said knowingly.

"Well, not exactly earthbound, because nothing really *binds* them to the earth."

"Except their own lack of faith in existence beyond death and their own desire for the security of the physical body," said Sharma.

"Yes, right," said Diane, smiling. "And except the mediums themselves."

"Hogwash," Bob said.

"Well, it might be hogwash," Melissa said, "but the fact is that we're contacting spirits at Arny's house. And they do a lot more than talk."

I wanted to get back to the earthbound spirits. What did Diane mean the mediums themselves bind the spirits to the earth? Sharma had said something similar, and I worried again that I might be hindering Zena's progress out of the astral plane.

"Probably not," Diane said. "Since you are the first in a hundred years to contact them at all, they most likely are locked in by their own problems. But spirits who ordinarily would pass quickly through the transitory zones can be detained by people who want to hold on to them. It truly is harmful."

"Why do people want to contact the dead any-way?" asked Bob. "It's morbid."

"Sentimentality," explained Diane. "They might feel remorse for treating a relative wrongly and want to apologize. Or they might want to just hold on to them a little longer."

"Or," said Sharma, "they might make the mistake of thinking they can obtain information about the other side."

I looked at her, knowing she was talking about me.

She continued: "People have the mistaken assumption that just because someone passes out of this life into another, he suddenly becomes very intelligent and full of universal wisdom. It's absolutely untrue. A foolish person will die and become a foolish spirit."

"Until he was evolved over a period of many lifetimes," Diane added.

The two women were getting along very well, I noticed. I had not seen Sharma so pleased with a discussion of these matters in a long time. I smiled at her, and she was forced to return the smile.

Melissa brought lunch in a couple of baskets which she handed to Bob and Diane to carry to the beach. Hank brought the cooler, which was filled with white wine and more iced tea, and lots of fresh, crisp vegetables. Melissa carried the blanket; I was put in charge of the beach umbrella, since I was the one who had been complaining about the heat.

During lunch, Diane asked if she might be invited to sit in during one of our sessions.

I avoided answering directly. What I really wanted was to have a session again just with Michael. I tried to be as diplomatic as possible.

"What do you mean, you're going to do the Ouija alone tonight?" said Melissa, one of those people who refused to take no for an answer.

"I think I would like to have a very quiet session tonight," I replied. "There have been so many disturbances recently that it has been very difficult to reach Zena. We may have lost her altogether."

"You crazies are talking as if these are actual people who exist," said Bob.

"Well, *something* has been contacting us on the Ouija board," said Melissa.

"Come on," said Bob. "Someone obviously is a sleight-of-hand artist. Perhaps there are true mediums, which I doubt, but certainly you're not going to find one in the middle of the beach on Fire Island."

"But it's true, Bob," said Melissa. "You've got to show him, Arny. You've got to prove it to him."

"Arnold doesn't have to prove it to anyone," said Hank. "You're getting excited again."

"That's the real trouble, Melissa," I said. "When you get excited—whenever any of us becomes overinvolved in the Ouija—everything goes berserk. Let me do one session alone with Michael, just to see if we can get Zena back with us."

"He might be right," said Diane to Melissa. "From what you've told me, I imagine that the energy level in that room went off the Richter scale. It might be a good idea to let them do it alone."

"Oh please, Arny," said Melissa. "So what if we don't reach Zena tonight? You can try alone next week. The main thing is that we reach some spirits, that we make contact with the other world. I want Bob to see."

"Wait a minute," Diane said. "That's rather dangerous thinking. Getting involved with the spirit world is no parlor game. If you allow yourself to become emotionally wrapped up in it, you could open yourself to real trouble."

"What trouble?" asked Melissa contemptuously. "I'm stronger than any of them." My impulse was to contradict her, but I had no wish to begin an argument.

"You could make yourself vulnerable to obsession," said Diane.

"Obsession! What's that?" Bob asked.

"It's when a spirit attaches itself to you and lives through your body. It's only a counterfeit life for them, but they'd rather have that than the limbo they're in now."

"I thought that was possession, when a spirit takes over your body," said Hank.

"It's quite the same thing," said Diane. "The entity takes you over to one degree or another. If it is in complete control, that's total possession."

"But what can it do to you?"

"I suppose it depends on your strength of will. If you're weak, it might prey upon your weaknesses, turn you into an alcoholic, or a drug addict, or a sex maniac, or make you hyperviolent; even, in extreme cases, make you mentally ill. If you're stronger, it might just drain your energy, give you headaches, insomnia, make you tired all the time."

"Nothing a little Geritol couldn't take care of," Hank remarked, grinning. Melissa shot him a look.

"Well, I'm certainly strong enough to take care of myself," she said. "How about this: We all will come, but we won't participate. We'll just watch you and Michael work the board."

I hesitated. I really didn't want them around.

"Please. I'd really love to see how it operates," said Diane. "And so would Bob, though he never would admit it."

215

"If it's so damned dangerous," asked Bob, "why are you so anxious?"

"Actually," she said, "it's true that when you participate you give the spirits energy, and if you give them energy you give them life. But if we *don't* participate and only watch, we'll just be observers."

Melissa told them about the evening of the flying ashtray with its lighted candle—the first inkling we had had of the physical power these spirits could generate.

"That's exactly what I mean," said Diane. "It was your being so involved with them—and so furious, I think—that gave them the energy to be able to do that." Melissa was stilled; I think it was the first time she realized her own responsibility for the occurrence.

"I believe Arnold ought to stop the séances altogether," said Sharma. "But he won't. He keeps trying to obtain more information. He thinks he can learn all about the otherworld. His life has been threatened and he's almost died twice as a result of the spirits. But still he goes on."

"You know that spirits can be very tricky," Diane said to me kindly, seeing that I was a bit put off by Sharma's remark. "They make it impossible for one to obtain accurate information. They lead you on, but nothing can be believed. It's all an illusion."

"What does that mean?" asked Bob.

"They'll say anything, just to attract attention and interest," she said. "If you're interested, you'll keep coming back to them, and they'll be able to keep feeding off your energy."

"You mean that Zena may not be telling the truth?" I asked. It didn't make sense. Her story had been totally consistent from the beginning, and Beth's and Higgins's interference seemed to be aimed at preventing Zena from telling it. All Zena kept asking us was to please tell the truth. But what if Diane was correct? What if there was no truth, if the whole performance was just a ploy to keep themselves near the physical existence they craved? The whole thing suddenly became very ugly, like a lewd sexual relationship where the partners feed on one another, depraved, dehumanized, obscene. If Zena was feeding on our energies, and we allowed it, then there was something very wrong with us. It was not a pretty thought.

"All of you are basing this whole discussion on reincarnation," Bob pointed out. "What if you just don't believe in it?"

"There are no proofs, Bob. One can only believe intuitively," Diane replied, "since true belief comes only from inner experience."

"Also, there's the possibility that Arny and his friends are living a fantasy they all want to believe in," said Hank, "and that none of it actually happens at all."

"Come on, what about the flying ashtray?" Melissa countered, bristling. "Nobody imagined that."

"Then," said Bob, "I suppose you could say it's all a product of the strange workings of the human mind. Psychokinesis I think it's called. People who move things with their brain power."

"The spirits you think you have contacted could even be entities that *already* have attached themselves to you," said Diane.

"Come on," I said. "None of us is possessed."

"Oh, but there's no way of knowing that," said Sharma. "Thousands of people live with entities attached to them. It's a part of one's karma that is not fully understood."

"And," Diane added, "when you do the Ouija, you give the entity energy and a voice." I looked at her. What they were saying made me reel.

"Do you mean to have us believe that there are people alive now who are possessed, going through life with invisible beings attached to them?" asked Hank, evidently as incredulous as I.

"That's right," Sharma said. "Thousands of people. Maybe millions."

"Well, I don't believe a word of it," Bob said, getting up and stretching. "But I certainly want to see it work. How about it, Arny?" After a discussion like that, how could I turn them down?

The conversation had stretched on for hours. It was still very hot, but somewhat cooler than when we arrived. We could walk on the sand now, so we hooked our fingers through the straps of our sandals, gathered up the blankets and baskets and carried them back to the house. Sharma and I arranged with the four of them to meet at our house at eight. We planned to have dinner togather, then introduce Bob and Diane to the Ouija.

During our walk home Sharma took a new tack in her appeal to quit. She said the spirits were boorish, and criticized their language. She did not sound like the Sharma who was worldly-wise. "It's dangerous, it's disgusting, and I abhor listening to their vileness."

"Well, if it's so unpleasant for you," I said rather unkindly, "why don't you take a book and go into the other room and read?" She stopped and caught my hand with hers.

"No," she said. "I won't leave you."

That evening François was in a snit because he had made plans to go out with friends, not realizing that Robert Chambers would be our dinner guest.

Everyone arrived on schedule. Hank started to say that on thinking it over he preferred to go dancing instead, but he was quickly silenced by Diane and Melissa. I had already spoken with Michael, who was all in favor of our working the Ouija alone, with the others just watching. We had a light supper and then we began.

We set up particularly carefully that night. Not only because Bob and Diane were there, but because we wanted to be sure to be in the correct frame of mind. Our goal was to reach Zena, and to hold her without interference from Beth or Higgins. Michael and I geared our minds to that end. We directed people to specific chairs that we had set back from the table. I turned off the living-room lights and lit the candle while Michael carefully touched up the letters and numerals of the board, all under the fascinated and scrutinizing eyes of our guests. I asked Sharma formally if she would take notes for us, and she agreed. Then Michael and I sat down in the darkened room.

We did not invoke the spirits; there had been no need to since that first night when, on a whim, we had invited them into our lives. But as Michael and I reached out to touch the inverted glass in the hushed, candle-lit room, I breathed one word:

"Zena."

The energy was characteristically smooth and flowing, and the glass immediately sped around the letters as it had at our first meeting. I felt comfortable with this energy. The decision to work the Ouija only with Michael had been a good one. The glass spelled quickly and I called out the letters to Sharma. Michael was totally absorbed in the board. The others remained silent, watching.

YOU HAVE BROUGHT NEW FRIENDS ROBERT DIANE I AM PLEASED MORE KNOW TRUTH

Diane was delighted that her name had been spelled; Bob was astounded. He suspected, however, that we were pushing the glass.

"You two probably had this arranged before we arrived," he said. There was only one way to convince him and get on with the séance. I invited him to put his finger on the glass, very lightly. I told him to clear his mind of everything, to sit quietly for a moment, concentrating on nothing but the feeling of an imaginary space between his fingertips and the glass. He touched the glass and sat quietly, his expression concentrated—then relaxed. He was ready. I replaced my finger on the glass, as did Michael. It took off at top speed around the letters. We struggled to keep up with it; there could be no doubt in Bob's mind now that the energy was coming from some outside source. He felt the power through his body just as we did.

"Is this thing that knows our names the one you have been dealing with all summer?" Bob asked. He seemed to find it difficult to speak, he was concentrating so hard on keeping up with the speeding glass. As if in reply, the glass flashed out four letters.

ZENA

Bob was flabbergasted. "Do you think she knows where we come from and what we do?" Again the glass zigzagged across the board, spelling out its message. It was easy for me to read as the letters were touched, so familiar had I become with this kind of communication. But I called the letters for Sharma to write, so the others could know the message, too.

YES YOU ARE AN ACTOR

"Do you know who I have just worked with?"

NO

I was sure Zena could have told us the names

of both his costars if she had wanted to, and that "No" simply meant she had other matters to discuss. I knew Bob was still involved in examining the phenomenon he had encountered, in testing it. But Zena did not have much time. That she had managed to be here and unmolested by Beth was a miracle. It had been risky to invite Bob onto the board with us. The glass moved to the letter ring again.

PLEASE TELL MY STORY SO LONELY DEATH SO LONG IN SEA

Zena spelled out her story once more, and I helped, explaining the details of her cryptic Ouija shorthand: Beth's illegitimate child, her great shame, Zena's acceptance of the child, the resentment and hostility she felt toward her sister, Beth's involvement with Higgins the captain—a relationship that allowed, if not caused, the death of two people they loved.

Strange that I had used the word: love. If Beth hated her sister Zena, she must have loved her, too, for isn't that the way of all siblings? It struck me that part of Beth's torment was that she was punishing herself for allowing Zena's death. Perhaps she had not wanted her sister to die, nor her daughter to perish in flames in the sea. All she wanted was to be more important, to be loved, for once more than Zena. She traveled in the captain's quarters while her sister rode below in steerage—but perhaps leaving her to die when the ship caught fire at sea was not part of the plan. Had Higgins prevented her from going below to save them? Had her own fear stopped her from making the attempt? Or was it just impossible—would it have been suicide for her to attempt a rescue? Perhaps Beth had been wrongly accused: That could be Zena's illusion, too, the illusion of martyrdom.

And now Beth was paying the price. Thinking herself evil, she became evil. She became her image of herself, and she would exist in this image for hundreds, perhaps thousands of years, until she realized what she was doing to herself.

Suddenly there was a jerking of the energy flow, and the glass struggled and faltered. Beth was there. Zena had not been allowed a complete session without her.

EVIL BETH IS EVIL DO NOT ALLOW HER A struggle as the glass was wrenched out of our range, out of Zena's control. A struggle. A pause. Diane flinched and shivered.

DO NOT ALLOW HER Another pause. Another struggle.

"What's happening?" said Bob. "What's going on?"

"It's Beth," whispered Michael. "Feel the cold."

I CANNOT CONTROL PLEASE TELL MY STORY I CANNOT STAY TELL TRUTH I CANNOT And the energy ceased. It was over.

Bob was perspiring from the energy of concentration. Michael looked remarkably refreshed and said he felt exhilarated.

"It worked," he said. "It was like in the beginning. The energy was good."

Bob looked at me, baffled.

"Amazing" was all he could say. "Amazing."

Friday, August 11

The next week was exceptionally busy. I seemed to have a million jobs to do and, in addition, with Bob in town there was something happening every night. I decided to give a large party at my place on Wednesday evening. Mutual friends of Bob's and mine were invited—movie people, actors, actresses, socialites, diplomats. Among the guests were Lynn Redgrave, Chita Rivera, Yolande Bavan, and Richard Chamberlain. Yolande was a good friend and had visited us upon occasion at Fire Island.

It was everything a party should be—glamorous, upbeat, and a terrific success. My apartment had been photographed for magazines, but while it always looked handsome, filled with people it was sensational. There were always fresh flowers and candles, but that night I added more—green ferns in the fireplaces, the insides of which were freshly whitewashed for the summer, and huge arrangements of white geraniums and spiky blue delphiniums. And dozens of white candles, all blazing. Outside, an old brick-walled garden full of trees and planted with periwinkle, ivy, and boxwood was lit with white paper globes like moons floating on the surface of the ivy, making the greens dark and shiny against the midnight-blue sky. I believed that a party ought to be a special occasion. When you walked in the door, you should be entering another world, created just for that evening. It took a great deal of preparation: arranging for the bartender and maids; planning the menu; finding and arranging the flowers; rearranging the furniture to accommodate so many people; and one of the most important things of all, selecting the appropriate music. For this evening I chose light, bright Baroque—Couperin, Telemann, arrangements of Vivaldi for guitar, harpsichord, and string orchestra—all fast and brilliant. And for after dinner, nineteenth-century waltzes. I usually kept the food rather simple. That evening it was a huge salade niçoise served in an enormous antique wooden dough bowl and full of fresh shrimp and several kinds of vegetables. With it we had cheese, French bread, bowls of fruit, and a dessert that Sharma made: English custard with gooseberries, called Gooseberry Fool.

It was a very lively party. Much laughter and lighthearted conversation, very little seriousness. Diane caught up with me at one point and began asking more questions about how I had become involved with the Ouija, proclaiming that I must be very psychic. I didn't know—I didn't feel psychic. Somehow, it all had just happened. The conversation lasted about three minutes before I was pounded on the back by an actor friend and we launched into stories of happenings on the Coast. It was an evening for Bob to see his New York friends he had not seen recently, and for people who liked each other to be together.

About midway through the evening, I went out for a breath of air and stood just outside the big windows, on the steps leading down into the garden. A beautiful sight: women in silk saris and long cotton dresses, their colors flashing darkly in the glow of the moonlike spheres of light. A breeze wafted in from the river, making a rustling sound in the trees, cooling the August air. In the garden and in the house, I could hear the voices of alive, happy people, snatches of conversation, peals of laughter, the stirring of ice in glasses. I felt refreshed and very much at peace with myself. After a few moments, I went back inside.

The party broke up about two in the morning. It took the help a bit longer to finish the last of the glasses and put away the food. When the place was empty, I fell into bed, blissfully exhausted.

The next day I took care of a few business matters, but mostly I relaxed. Sharma and I decided to spend the evening at my apartment, eating leftover salade niçoise and cheese and watching a late-night talk show. Bob had told us the evening before that he would appear on the program to promote his film, after which he would be heading for England and more work. I've never been much of a television watcher, so while the program was on, I sorted through my portfolio, reorganizing photos and other material to show a new client. Bob was the second or third guest. He looked terrific, very relaxed, well dressed as always. He was extremely articulate and charming. When the host set up the conversation about the movie, Bob dutifully mentioned the names of all the people he had worked with, the film's release date, and what a treat it had been to work with his two costars.

Then I heard Bob say something startling—that he had just experienced the most extraordinary thing: He had sat in on a séance.

"Sharma, listen to this!" I said. "Listen to what he's saying."

He obviously took the host by surprise. Sharma and I looked at one another in disbelief. The host wanted to know if it was a séance with a black curtain and a medium, but Bob explained that it had taken place on an ordinary table in an ordinary room, with people he knew. He related Zena's story and even commented how surprised he had been by the detail of the messages. He revealed the scandal over Rosamond, Beth's lies and Zena's shame, the illicit romance with Higgins, the fiery deaths. He told the story as if he were talking about living people, people he knew.

The host asked how much investigating Bob

had done into the legitimacy of our Ouija. Weren't we pushing the glass? Couldn't the entire thing have been set up? All the normal questions one would ask. Bob answered them all, dealing with the doubts one by one. He admitted that he had not believed it until he had participated himself and had actually felt the exhilarating energy of the contact.

We listened—and millions of other people listened—as he told of the experience in tones of wonder, intellectual bewilderment, and helpless belief. He believed because he had to: It had happened to him.

Sharma and I were thunderstruck. We were hearing our own experience. After all those weeks of being hushed up and more or less undercover, our séances were being publicized on nationwide television. It was absolutely incredible.

The minute the next guest appeared on the program, the telephone rang. It was Michael, who could scarcely catch his breath because of the excitement. Zena was famous.

Late the following afternoon, I herded Rachel and Joshua into the back seat of the car, threw an empty suitcase into the trunk, and wove my way uptown to pick up Howard and Michael on my way out to the country. François would join us there. The suitcase was for clothing I would be taking home on Sunday evening. This was to be my last weekend at the summer house before my trip to Europe the following week.

I had mixed thoughts about leaving the Ouija. I still had an unsettled, unsatisfied feeling about it. I wanted to continue, although I knew that leaving it was in my best interests. Even so, I found myself wondering during the drive how the others were going to get along without me. Michael, I was sure, would want to pursue it.

"Oh, maybe we'll get Melissa to sit in with us," he said tentatively.

I asked him to keep records so I could be filled in when I returned—and he promised to let me know immediately if anything amazing occurred.

For myself, I knew I needed a vacation, and I was looking forward to seeing my English friends in London, and then joining several American friends for a tour of the Loire. I wondered if I would miss the Ouija and these weekly sessions at the beach. Time would tell.

Michael asked me if I would be traveling near Liverpool. We all laughed.

Traffic was very heavy, and the afternoon very hot. We were tired before we left, having worked all day, and the long drive was even more exhausting. We sat quietly for the most part, busy with our private thoughts. Nobody wanted to cook that evening, so we stopped at a seafood place in Sayville for dinner before boarding the ferry across to the Island.

The bay breezes as we churned across were a welcome relief from the hot, still air of the mainland. At the house, François had opened all the windows and was sitting with a book, reading and listening to music. François had not called after Bob's appearance on television; it turned out, much to his chagrin, that he had missed the program. Michael and I told him about it, and even Howard joined in with some enthusiasm. As we talked, Michael began setting up the board for that evening's session. Now that Zena's story was known, we were anxious to contact her. We found ourselves freshly interested, eager to learn.

I was feeling very much alive and alert. I walked out to the deck and breathed deeply, smelling the ocean's salty breezes and listening to its pounding rhythm. Then I put the dogs to bed and helped Michael prepare the table.

François was the first to take a seat. I suppose it was Bob's television appearance that gave him new confidence. Or perhaps it had just made the Ouija seem more important, given it a new perspective for him. I cautioned François that he absolutely must keep his head. I think I offended him, but I felt it was necessary.

Michael lit the candle and sat down across the table from me. Howard flicked off the light and took his place. We sat quietly for a moment. Howard was relaxed, waiting to write, absolutely unconcerned; Michael was deep in concentration, preparing himself; François's eyes shifted nervously in the half-light. I could see the old fear enveloping him; I almost suggested that he not sit in with us, but I felt it would hurt him needlessly, so I just hoped that he would be able to maintain his composure. I wanted to do one thing: contact

Zena. There were questions I wanted answered, and I didn't have much time.

Ritualistically, I reached across and touched the glass with my index finger; Michael, and then François, hesitant, did the same.

"Zena," I said. "Are you here? Please be with us."

MY FRIEND YOU HAVE TOLD

Zena was cut off by an erratic and powerful surge of energy I recognized as Higgins; the glass veered wildly away from the board. When it returned, the messages were abusive and mocking. Beth began lashing out at François, whose eyes widened with anger although he fought to control himself.

"Zena," I said firmly. "We wish to speak with Zena only."

YOU HAVE RUINED YOU HAVE LIED YOU WILL BE STOPPED

"You cannot stop us," I said. "Where is Zena?"

The glass tugged itself across the board, maddeningly out of control. The letters it touched made no sense. The force I felt was like anxiety, or extreme agitation. I wanted relief, either a strong flow or a total cessation. I could not stand this feeling much longer.

"Zena," I called out, illogically speaking louder to make her hear. The energy stopped, then began again, flowing smoothly.

NO TIME FRIENDS DONT LET THEM I NEED TO TELL YOU ARNOLD NO TIME DO NOT GO

"Do not go?" I asked, almost inaudibly.

The awful battle continued, Zena and Beth struggling for control, Zena's every fitful, faltering message brutally interrupted by Beth's obscenities against me, against Howard, but mostly against François. François became more and more furious. He pointed at the board, cursing it. "*Cochonne!*" he screamed at Beth, pushing back from the table.

"François, stop it!" I said. "Don't let yourself become involved with them."

Beth called François a faggot, a weakling.

I WILL TAKE YOU YOU WILL BE NO MORE

"What does that mean?" François asked, out of his mind with terror and rage.

"Calm down, François," I shouted. "It means nothing. Please . . ."

"You're trying to control me," he screamed. "You let them insult me. I won't let them. You can't control me. You bastard, you filthy bastard . . ."

Suddenly he dove across the table at me, his eyes wild in the light of the flame. He grabbed for me, shouting curses. Howard was on his feet instantly, trying to hold him back, fighting to control him. François was incredibly strong; his eyes were fierce. Above us, the huge black iron chandelier began flashing on and off, on and off. I couldn't speak. Without warning, the chandelier tore loose from the ceiling and crashed down on the table, grazing François's arm. He barely reacted to the blow, but the dogs in the back began barking in alarm.

In the next instant, François's body stiffened.

His jaw went rigid, his face became expressionless, then contorted in a hideous mask. His teeth clenched and he could not speak, but his voice made low, stuttering sounds, stifled, petrifying. It was like an attack of epilepsy—his arms seemed paralyzed, his fingers rigidly extended, and his eyes rolled upward, back into his head.

"My God," said Michael hoarsely. I couldn't think what to do. Howard struggled to keep François from me. Michael dove at him and struck him hard in the face. The monstrous face contorted itself even more in a terrible struggle, and then it was François again, weak, helpless, spent. Whatever it was was gone.

Howard guided him to the sofa; someone turned on a light. François could not speak, and his face was vacant and lifeless. Michael brought water to him. François continued to lie on the sofa, his eyes open and void.

"He's in a state of shock," said Howard. "His skin is cold. He's trembling."

Slowly, François gained control of himself, although he did not speak. We talked to him, trying to sound reassuring. I couldn't tell whether he was aware of what had happened. He seemed very foggy, clearly not entirely coherent. We stayed with him for a while, then Michael helped him to bed. When Michael came out, Howard fixed drinks for the three of us. I let the burning liquid flow down my throat—it was all I could do to swallow.

"Arny, are you all right?" Howard asked. "I had no idea he was that strong."

"It wasn't François's strength, it was Beth," said Michael. "Or Higgins. Somebody had him." I didn't want to believe that. It was too much for me to accept that he had actually been attacked by a spirit.

"No, he couldn't have been possessed," I said, helpless. "But that face, that horrible face."

"It wasn't François's face, Arny."

There was no sense trying to figure things out. We all had been knocked out by the experience, all of us drained.

"We really are playing with fire," Howard said. "This is it. No more." I knew he was right. But Zena, her plea. She had appealed to me by name just before that awful episode. And François. If only he hadn't involved himself we might have known what Zena wanted. I began to hate François—and then to hate myself for it. I shook my head, jammed with short-circuited ideas, frustrations, guilt. There was no point in sorting anything out tonight. I stood up and walked past the chandelier, lying awry on the dining table, naked wires protruding threatening from the chipped and gaping hole in the ceiling. We would deal with that in the morning.

FOURTEENTH ENCOUNTER

Saturday, August 12

It was half light, and I was still in bed. Half
awake, half asleep, drifting in that vast intermedi-
ate cloud. Something was wrong. A terrible anxiety seized me, and I began to feel chilled. I saw a
face in the darkness, twisted and anguished. I re-
coiled, and the face dissolved into the dim light. I
sat up, holding the memory of the face and a crash
of metal and glass on the table. But which was
real, which was the dream?

I got up, pulled on my swimming trunks, and
went into the dining room to see. The huge black
iron chandelier was lying across the scarred table.
In the center of its iron ring was the juice glass,
miraculously untouched. Only one of the bulbs
was broken. Carefully, I picked up the splinters of
glass and disposed of them. Then I lifted the fix-
ture off the table. It was extremely heavy and took

a great deal of strength. I placed it gently in a corner of the room, leaning it against the wall. I felt the surface of the table with my fingers. It was deeply gashed where the chandelier had struck. I found some tape for the ends of the exposed wires that protruded from the hole in the ceiling. I stood on the table and taped the live ends carefully, splaying them apart from one another. I taped over the dimmer control also. This completed, I stood contemplating the table with its evil ring of characters. Suddenly decisive, I went to get a sponge and some cleanser. As I began to scrub the surface, I remembered Zena's words. I needed to know her final message. What had she been trying to tell me? It wasn't finished. Not yet. I couldn't bring myself to erase the board. I took the cleanser back to the kitchen and covered the table with a cloth. I had all day to think.

I started some water for coffee and took Rachel and Joshua to the beach. When I returned, the water was boiling, and Howard was scooping coffee into the filter. Michael walked past us without saying a word and stood in front of the dining room. He shook his head.

"What do you think we ought to do?" he asked.

"Just leave it where it is," I answered. "I'll call the landlord on Monday. How is François?"

"Seems O.K., I guess," Michael told us. "He's still asleep, but he looks all right."

We had some breakfast and took our coffee and a couple of blankets out onto the beach. About an hour later François emerged from the house and came down to join us. He was rubbing a large bruise on his arm, but other than that he looked very healthy and surprisingly refreshed. He kept looking at his arm.

"What the hell happened to my arm?" he asked.

"Don't you remember your argument with the spirits last night?" I asked. "And that the chandelier fell and hit you?"

He was shocked.

Michael began to say something more. I gestured for him to play it down, sensing it might be too distressing. François obviously did not remember anything. And as far as I was concerned, it all would remain a mystery to him.

"How did the light fall?" he wanted to know. I walked with him back to the house. He stared blankly at the bent chandelier, the dented table. He didn't go very near the table. Clearly he was disturbed.

"Don't you remember any of it?" I asked. François only shook his head. He remembered nothing.

"I told you," he said resentfully. "I knew this would happen; it's not my fault." For the first time that summer I felt twinges of compassion for François. He was right—it really wasn't his fault.

We walked back to the beach to join the others, who could see that François was shaken.

"Don't worry about it," Howard said. "It's not going to happen again. Let's drop the whole subject." We dropped it. But I knew that it wasn't finished. Somehow I must get to Zena once more.

François left to visit other friends that afternoon. I spent most of the day on the beach. I took a walk with the dogs, and nearly reached Water Island before I realized how far I'd come. I decided to visit Melissa and Hank, say good-bye, and tell them what had happened the night before. I returned to the house and was engrossed in packing when Michael came into the room.

"What are we going to do about tonight?" he asked.

"I don't know," I answered doubtfully. "As far as I'm concerned, we've got to find out what Zena was trying to tell us. How can I go to Europe with this thing unsettled? But François will never go along with it."

"Neither will Howard," Michael said.

When François returned later that afternoon, he told us he had accepted an invitation for dinner and would be home late. He changed clothes and left again. Michael and I relaxed. The big problem had been solved. We prepared a good dinner together—salad and some veal cooked in lemon and butter sauce. At dinner, we persuaded Howard to do one more session with us.

"You must be crazy after what happened last night," he said.

"But that was because of François," Michael pointed out. Howard wasn't easy to convince—but we wanted him to stay and record the proceedings. I wanted very much to concentrate all my efforts on the Ouija, and on contacting Zena. We appealed to him. It was going to be my last chance. Howard drove a hard bargain: We were to insist on speaking to nobody but Zena, and if that proved impossible, or if there was even the hint of trouble, we would stop. And that would be the end of it. We agreed.

It was late, as usual, when the room was cleared and the board was ready to begin. Michael and I took extra time to prepare ourselves and concentrate on the energy that would bring Zena to us. I tried not to feel anxious about it. I put myself into a relaxed frame of mind, and filled myself with confidence that she would come. We placed our fingertips on the glass.

The flow of energy was instantaneous and gratifyingly smooth. The glass sped around the letters as it had the first night. I knew I didn't have much time.

"Zena!" I said. "What did you want to tell us?" The glass began to move.

ARNOLD HOWARD MICH

But at that moment our concentration was broken by a sound at the door. We turned to see François standing immobile, shocked at what we were doing, not knowing whether to protest or turn and run. I thought fast, not wanting to break the mood we had established with Zena.

"It's all right, François," I said quietly. "Zena is here. Come in. It's all right. Look, she's saying our names." Slowly, he came toward the table and stood looking down at it. I drew in a breath.

"Zena, we are all here now," I said. "We are listening. Tell us." The glass responded instantly, the energy smooth and exhilarating, the letters clear:

THANK YOU MY FRIENDS FOR TELLING TRUTH RELEASING ME NOW THE WORLD KNOWS NOW I CAN REST GOODBYE MY FRIENDS ARNOLD HOWARD FRANCOIS MICHAEL I HAVE BROUGHT YOU GIFT FROM MY GRAVE

The energy stopped. We knew it was over.

We sat back in our chairs, looking at one another, not speaking. I felt relieved but a little sad. The séances had been an incredible experience, though at what cost I could not begin to assess. Zena had thanked us and had said good-bye. She was gone; to which realm—to which plane— had she escaped to continue on her journey? And for the rest of us—François, Melissa—would we ever know what price any of us had paid? In spite of everything, there were still no answers.

Michael took the yellow pad from Howard and read Zena's final message.

"A gift from my grave," he repeated puzzled. "What do you suppose she meant?" An enigmatic message, probably a symbol of her thanks, but it didn't seem to matter anymore. We all went into the living room and collapsed on the sofas.

Suddenly Michael leaned forward and motioned toward the coffee table. We all stared. There in the center was a little pool of water, and in it lay a starfish, pulsating rhythmically. I blinked and leaned forward for a closer look.

"Where did it come from?" François asked in astonishment.

We looked at one another, afraid to say the words.

François picked up the starfish and gently placed it on the small crystal egg that lay on the table. The tiny creature wrapped its perfectly shaped tentacles reflexively around the egg and clung to it with its last strength.

EPILOGUE

Our house, and the one next door where Max and Annie lived, were both owned by the same man. After that summer, we never rented our house again, but Max returned to his every year until 1974. One day he told me that Zena's release had not meant the end of spirits on Fire Island: We had left Beth and Higgins. Max had no doubt of their continued presence.

Max owned an antique Thai angel that had a tradition as guardian of houses in Thailand centuries ago. Each autumn when he left the house for the winter, he took all his belongings to the city with the exception of the angel, which he left to protect the house. At the end of the summer of 1974 he decided not to take the house again the following year. When he closed up for the last time in the fall, he took with him his Thai angel.

Four days later his house and the one we had rented burned to the ground. The fire department learned that the fire had begun in our house, but was unable to determine the cause.

Before this extraordinary summer began, we knew very little of the possibility of existence on any other plane, or whether there was, indeed, any life after death. Certainly none of us had considered reincarnation or believed we would be born again. This experience opened our minds to the possibilities of other states of existence, the irrelevance of time, and the chance that some form of life does exist for the human spirit in another dimension. Certainly each of us, sooner or later, felt the presence of an unknown force, an energy we could neither define nor control. All we knew for sure was that something unreal, something inexplicable, happened to each of us that summer.

And it wasn't only in our minds: There was that bizarre photograph I took at Max's dinner party, with the images of the uninvited guests. The photo remained in Max's possession. And there was the starfish, which nobody could explain. As for the messages that came to us on the Ouija board—"Logs records Liverpool log red night deep inside; Book red and green; By the large hill today read of log red night"—they themselves were a phenomenon. Our human perception and understanding simply could not interpret such messages.

When the summer was over, we realized that perhaps François had been right all along in warning us against the Ouija and the evils it could unleash. The rest of us felt guilty about forcing the séances on him. We decided that he should have the starfish, and gave it to him with the unspoken hope that he would forgive us the pain we had caused him.

Since that summer, I have been asked by friends and acquaintances to preside over parlor-game séances. I have always been reluctant, but I did allow myself to be persuaded again. We proceeded as we had that summer, and succeeded in contacting spirits. But the results were disastrous. One of the company fainted from the shock and strain, and one woman became violently ill. I learned later from others who had had experiences with séances that often spirits will immediately search out the weakest, most vulnerable person in the room and try to possess his mind and body.

On one other time, at Melissa's and Hank's apartment in town, we tried an experiment. They made a Ouija board and, with me sitting across the room, tried to contact a spirit. They were immediately successful and the board began telling a story about a relation of mine who had died in New York City years earlier. Then it gave his wife's name and the names of various members of the family, including my own great grandparents. Melissa and Hank had no knowledge of my genealogy. They spelled the letters out loud and I wrote them down from across the room, unable to see the board. We were amazed by this test.

The forces one deals with are of unknown power and proportions, and should be left utterly alone. I have never again attempted—nor will I ever—to contact the spirit world.

A.C.

June 1976: Since I was not acquainted with Arnold Copper at the time of his astonishing summer at Fire Island, my reporter's curiosity prompted me to do a bit of research on my own. During a two-week holiday in England, I telephoned a friend who worked at Lloyd's of London and asked him if he might be able to find any information on a ship out of Liverpool, bound for New York, and wrecked en route. I did not know the exact name of the vessel, but I knew the captain: Higgins. And the year: 1873. My friend was delighted to help with such a mysterious request. A few days later he called me at my hotel. The report: That year there were some English ships which sailed from Liverpool and suffered casualties en route to the United States. And of these, a few were wrecked off the coast of Long Island, several being captained by men named Higgins! Was one of them *our* Captain Higgins?

C.L.

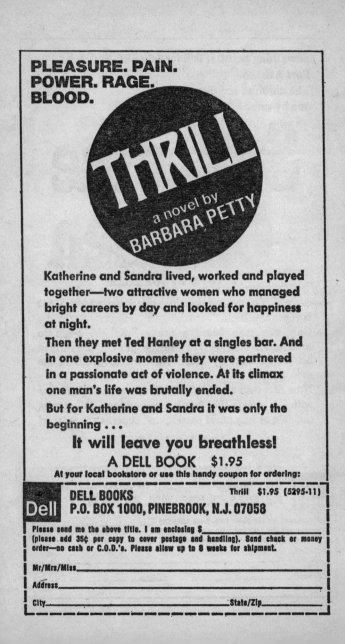

A young boy in the Catskills develops into a famous and breathtakingly skillful magician—with something to hide. His attempt to keep his secret from the public draws him onto a bizarre course that subtly leads into thrilling and psychologically terrifying regions.

MAGIC

A dazzling psychological thriller
by **William Goldman**
author of *Marathon Man*

A DELL BOOK $1.95

Dell Bestsellers